BECOMING BIO(

7 Steps To Increase
Unlock The Superhuman Within

LESTER SAVAGE

PRIMAL LIFE
ENJOY EVERYTHING, NEED NOTHING

BECOMING BIOCHEMICALLY SOBER
7 STEPS TO INCREASE HEALTH, HAPPINESS AND UNLOCK THE SUPERHUMAN WITHIN

LESTER SAVAGE

© 2018 PRIMAL LIFE INTERNATIONAL LTD

Published in the United Kingdom by
Primal Life International Ltd.
Plymouth Science Park, 1 Davy Road, Plymouth, PL6 8BX

There is an accompanying online course for this book.
Purchase online at:
www.LesterSavage.co.uk
www.LesterSavage.com

Lester Savage is available for speaking at events and private coaching. Please contact hello@lestersavage.com for further information.

ISBN 978-1-5272-2099-7

Preface

If you are reading this then it means you've taken an incredible leap forward towards creating a life that overflows with an abundance of energy, joy and freedom.

I cannot put into words the excitement I have for you and the remarkable journey that is yet to come your way. Simply by investing in Primal Life you are demonstrating your individual commitment to living a healthier, happier and stronger life and I believe that following these principles will take you there.

You've probably noticed that the logo for Primal Life is a leaping panther. For me nothing symbolises strength, power, grace and beauty as effectively as the panther does. But above all the panther represents what I hope Primal Life does for its members - freedom in all its abundance. Freedom to enjoy everything and need nothing. Freedom to explore life on our terms.

For several years now it has been my mission to uncover our capabilities as humans on an individual and societal plain. Physically, emotionally, intellectually and spiritually my research has shown that our potential is limitless.

As much as I would love to take credit for these principles, I am little more than a facilitator of tried and tested research. All the subjects mentioned in this book are proven principles and science has accepted them as standard knowledge. While you may not agree with everything you see or hear, take it for what it is – a second opinion. This journey you're about to embark on is simply about finding what works FOR YOU.

I'm truly privileged to have this opportunity to share with you the best of what I've learned. Enjoy this programme, but more importantly, use it! I want you to take full advantage of this book and the only way to really make this a life altering course you will never forget is by putting these principles into action. Show yourself what you are really made of and be the inspiration others need to see.

It's time to Enjoy Everything and Need Nothing – Starting Now!

Acknowledgements

This book took 8 years and 3 weeks to write. That isn't one lump sum of time. The book only took 3 weeks to write, yet I *needed* every event in the last 8 years to occur for this to come to fruition. I needed to experience depression, anxiety and shame. I needed to know what it's like to be morbidly obese. I needed to know what it was like to watch my family fall apart and rebound. I needed to "fail" over and over again. Looking back, this book and Primal Life could not have been born had those problems never occurred. For that, the first acknowledgement I must make is to all the problems that made me grow.

The next is to the real life idols like Richard Branson, Tony Robbins, Wim Hof, Elon Musk, Joe Rogan, Christopher Ryan, Yuval Noah Harari, Dave Asprey, Ben Greenfield, Neale Donald Walsh and Matthew Cahill. These people who in an integrative age have shown me, and millions like me, that there is another level to play the game we call life.

Next, it's to all those personally in my life that made this directly and indirectly come into fruition through their love and support. Mum (showing me I have the power to make a difference), Dad (the hours forcing me to listen to Zig Ziglar and Tony Robbins on long car journeys paid off – you never gave up on me), Casablanca (you keep me on my toes, keep me hungry and make me a proud brother). Best friends like Andy, Jack, Ed and Micky G. Rory, Elizabeth, Astra, Vin – having you as part of my tribe made me a better man. The Ashoka Kadampa Buddhist Centre. Lizzy the jungle queen who gave me "the island" and the Moseley family. Thank you.

Michael – It took 25 years to find myself a brother and best man. You were worth the wait. Thank you for "Being ma Sapien" and being the one to kickstart this journey for me.

To the scientists, doctors, guinea pigs, writers and unsung heroes that discover and explore the nature of existence through your research and then show us your findings.

Last but not least, James "JAMMY" Holden. Without you there is no Primal Life. You are an alchemist with the gift of turning my visions into reality. I'm privileged to have you as my business partner, my accountability buddy and my friend. This book marks a milestone in our growth together. One heck of a journey to come as we see how far we can really negotiate with reality. Here's to Enjoying Everything and Needing Nothing!

<u>Authors Note</u>

While I do believe and have seen proof that the information, exercises and advice I provide in this book can help you improve your overall health and happiness, please understand that not everyone will experience the exact same results. Every person is an individual and every situation is unique so no single piece of advice will work for everyone at every time. But I can confidently tell you that if you follow the steps in this book and continually apply them to your life, your chances of success increase dramatically.

The source notes for this book can be found in the "source notes" section in the back of this book. I do not use footnotes because this is not an academic book and I feel footnotes interfere with the ease of reading. Any names used when describing my personal interactions, such as with my clients, have been changed to protect their confidentiality.

<u>Important note from the Publisher</u>

Every effort has been made to obtain the necessary permissions with reference to copyright material, both illustrative and quoted. We apologise for any omissions in this respect and will be pleased to make the appropriate acknowledgements in any in any future edition.

Always consult your doctor before beginning the Primal Life Method or putting into practice any information provided by Lester Savage. The information provided in this book is published by Primal Life International Ltd and is not intended to diagnose any medical condition or to replace your healthcare professional. Always consult with your healthcare professional before changing your lifestyle/health. This includes the diet, exercise, breathing and cold exposure information provided by

Lester Savage. Always pick and follow a programme that best suits your personal medical requirements. If you experience any pain, discomfort or difficulty with the Primal Life Method you must stop and consult your healthcare provider.

The information contained within this book is for general information purposes only. The information is published by Primal Life International Ltd and while we endeavour to keep the information up to date and correct, we make no representations or warranties of any kind, express or implied, about the completeness, accuracy, reliability, suitability or availability with respect to the information or related graphics contained in the book for any purpose. Any reliance you place on such information is therefore strictly at your own risk.

In no event will Primal Life International Ltd or Lester Savage be liable for any loss or damage including without limitation, indirect or consequential loss or damage, or any loss or damage whatsoever arising out of, or in connection with, the use of this book.

Throughout this book we refer to other authors and information sources which are not under the control of Primal Life International Ltd. We have no control over the nature, content and availability of those sources. The inclusion of any external resource does not necessarily imply a recommendation or endorse the views expressed within them.

Contents

INTRODUCTION

    15   What Is Primal Life?
    19   Threshold
    21   Getting Started

SUPERHUMAN

    24   The Happy Caveman
    28   The Biochemical Superhuman
    31   What Is Health?
    33   Nature Vs Nurture
    35   Chapter Summary

THINK

    38   How The Brain Works
    43   The Stress Bucket
    45   Our Map Of The World
    49   Neuroplasticity
    53   Focus
    59   Sparkling Moment
    62   Logical Levels
    67   Identity
    73   Beliefs
    79   Questions & Language
    85   The Miracle Question
    90   Tracking Our Thoughts
    93   The Science Of Meditation
    98   Cultivating Gratitude
    100   A Compelling Future
    104   Swish Technique
    107   Cleaning Out The Past
    111   Achievement Vs Fulfilment
    116   Chapter Summary

BREATHE

121   The Primary Connection
124   Breath Awareness & Conscious Breathing
127   Our State
131   Mitochondria (Part 1)
133   Detox/Lymph System
135   Oxygen
138   Chapter Summary

MOVE

141   Movement Vs Exercise
144   The Brain Before Your Body
148   The Best Exercise
150   Born To Run
154   Strength
159   Chapter Summary

FUEL

162   Diets Don't Work
167   The Second Brain
171   Poisons
180   Vegetables And Fruit
184   Fat Burning Hero
191   Intermittent Fasting
195   Chapter Summary

COLD

201 A Warm And Comfy Caveman

204 Wim Hof The Iceman

207 Why Become An Iceman

210 Mitochondria (Part 2)

211 Sauna

213 Chapter Summary

CONNECT

215 Tribe

220 Community

223 The Illusion Of Connection

228 Choose Your Tribe

234 Shinrin Yoku

238 Mind/Body Connection

244 Chapter Summary

REST

247 The Importance Of Sleep

251 Sleep Hacks

254 Chapter Summary

THE SCIENCE OF HEALTH

256   Bad Science

TRACKING

259   Measuring Outcomes

PRIMAL PRACTICE

268   Morning Routine
270   The Talker & The Doer
275   Chapter Summary

APPENDIX

276   Glossary
285   Source Notes

<u>INTRODUCTION</u>

"You are one decision away from a totally different life"

Mark Batterson

What Is Primal Life?

What is the Primal Life Method? In short, it's all the best tools and techniques available for a holistic human transformation decoded and translated into an easy-to-follow formula. The word holistic comes from the word whole. In this context I'm referring to ways of improving your health and happiness by paying close attention to your body and mind, but also to your environment and important relationships. The Primal Life Method simplifies the most effective research into 7 simple principles which revitalise the way you think, act and feel on a day to day basis.

Now I'm proud to say that by fine tuning these principles into what we now know as the Primal Life Method I've been able to help countless people go through outstanding transformations. This isn't an attempt to brag, it's just quite obvious that when you're studying in-depth the best of what we know, whether it's philosophies from 2,500 years ago or the most up-to-date breakthroughs in neuroscience, you'd have to be blind not to see there are particular patterns and processes that are shared between them.

I've seen the Primal Life Method work time and time again with people from all ages, all backgrounds and all beliefs. It's helped people in their 80s who haven't been able to sleep at night, young college students looking to overcome their anxiety, to men and women in between who are looking to take their business to the next level or explore what else life has to offer.

I'm not a doctor, I'm your Primal Life coach; in essence I'm simply a facilitator. It would be wrong for me to take complete credit for this as I'm standing on the shoulders of giants who have conducted decades of research within key areas of physical and mental health. The reason this is so effective is not because I've magically come up with some system, it really is because they are tried and tested principles that on their own are effective, but combined can be life changing.

One of the most extreme examples I saw of the Primal Life Method having success was with a gentleman in his early 40s who was diagnosed with borderline personality disorder, bipolar, body dysmorphic disorder and severe depression and anxiety. He was taking a lot of medication at the time. He would wake up in a cold sweat every morning and for the first 2 hours each day he'd have a panic attack. He was constantly in fear with the belief that there was something wrong with one side of his face despite there being no issues. At one point I actually went to the hospital with him to see a specialist who confirmed there were no issues, but that didn't stop the overwhelming fear. I even had to hypnotise him in the car park just so he was in a more relaxed state to go into the appointment. With his bipolar he believed that for only three months of the year he'd feel in a good place and that the following 9 months would involve a spike of anxiety followed by a large dip of depression. After following the Primal Life Method for a few months he started to feel the best he had in years. The panic attacks stopped, the worry of his face had gone, and he woke up in the mornings feeling fresh, often finding himself on the tennis court by 7am.

This continued for approximately 6 months, however one week he came to see me because the way he was feeling had dipped. He continued to dip for the next 3 weeks, to the point that for the first time since following the method he started to talk about his face again. He believed this was down to the bipolar and that naturally this was the dip which was inevitably going to occur. I told him what I'll tell you now, that if we're going to make large claims about the quality of our life then we must act like scientists and test our theories. Coincidently for the 3 weeks he had dipped he had not been following the Primal Life Method. I told him the best way to test the theory would be to follow the method again and then if he hadn't improved, further help would be out of my jurisdiction as I am not a doctor. Sure enough, the following week when he came to see me after following the Primal Life Method as described in this course, he was back to his new happy self again.

The reason I'm so passionate about this topic is that it's very personal to me. 7 years ago I suffered from depression and anxiety. I was morbidly obese weighing 142 kilos (313 pounds or 22 and a half stone). I couldn't lift my own bodyweight, I'd get out of breath climbing stairs, I couldn't even tie my own shoelaces. Not only that but the way I felt was not just awful, I felt numb. I lived in this horrible studio apartment which was so small the only way I could cook was by sitting on my bed – breakfast in bed wasn't a luxury for me, it was a necessity! I was so ashamed of who I had become, I wouldn't let anyone come over. In fact, I found myself lying to my closest friends and family about where I lived, and the kind of life I was living. The awareness of mental health back then was a lot less known so I didn't know who I could speak to about the way I was feeling and to be honest, would probably have let my pride get in the way anyway... because I was just too ashamed. I genuinely believed that there was something inherently wrong with me. I'd forgotten all the times I'd been happy and thought maybe this is the way I am naturally wired to feel. It's ok for me now looking back and telling this story because I know that the future gets better. But at that time I remember feeling in such a state of uncertainty because I had no hope for the future.

Then something incredible happened.... I hit rock bottom. Well, I actually hit something which I now refer to as threshold. When it comes to overcoming any obstacle, threshold is so vital. So much so, that I want to dedicate a section to it in a moment.

My journey, my passion, my obsession if you will, led me on a whirlwind of personal growth. I read over 300 books ranging from neuroscience, biology, nutrition, fitness, psychology, philosophy and self-development. I immersed myself and trained in a number of different therapies, including neuro linguistic-programming, solution focused psychotherapy, cognitive behavioural therapy, hypnosis, yogic breathing, mindfulness and more. I travelled to Poland and spent time with the Iceman Wim Hof to learn how to endure sub-zero temperatures. I've even spent over a year living in a Buddhist centre to explore my spirituality. Doing these things didn't just make me feel better, it made me feel super-human. I didn't just transform my body, I transformed my mind.

Threshold

Threshold is a place where 3 specific things have to happen: you realise something has to change, that something is you, and that it has to happen now. You don't necessarily have to hit rock bottom to be at threshold, it's simply the turning point. In that moment I had 2 choices. Either I could keep living in my numb life, feeling ashamed with a body that didn't feel like my own, or I could recognise that if I wanted life to change, *I* would have to change.

What being at threshold gave me was the ability to make a decision. What I mean by a decision is the word in its purest form, which comes from the Latin root: De-caedere (de = cut, caedere = off), meaning to cut off from. The moment we've made a decision we've completely changed our life, haven't we? It may have taken time to build up to that moment, but when we finally say "No more!", "I quit", "I do" the course of our lives take a dramatic turn.

Simply by reading this book you've made a decision. What we're doing is immersing ourselves into a new environment which allows us to soak up a new strategy that doesn't just allow us to change, it allows us to grow.

In 1519 when the Spanish explorer Hernán Cortés arrived in Mexico to succeed in the Spanish conquest of the Aztec empire he made one of the biggest leadership decisions in history. He told his men to bore holes in the boats, sinking them. By cutting off the ability to retreat and forcing his men to follow him, within microseconds that decision raised their standards, increased their motivation and demanded the very best strategies from them if they were to succeed and avoid death. Why? Because there was no retreat. He had cut off the capacity to fail. It was either do or die.

In the past when people have come to me to stop smoking the first thing I'll always check is whether they're at threshold. Is their desire to stop smoking a 10 out of 10? If not, why not? If they're not at threshold, if their desire to smoking isn't a 10 out of 10, then I don't take them on as clients. Why? Because I can't make them do anything they don't want to do. I can only offer the right strategy. It's down to them, it's their responsibility in taking the right actions to get them where they want to be.

You may have heard me mention threshold before if you've attended one of my webinars. I say it to discourage people from buying books or my online course unless they are absolutely ready to commit. If someone is not at threshold, if they're not at a place yet where they're willing to be responsible for the change, then the chance for success of any strategy plummets.

Before we get properly into this book, you made an incredible decision to start the Primal Life Method. Just write down anywhere the moment that caused you to hit threshold. Take some time to reflect on where you were. Why did you make the decision to start The Primal Life Method? What are you committed to getting out of this book? Not just for yourself, but also for those you care about. Why are you really here?

Getting Started

You have already made such an important decision by purchasing this book and I want you to get maximum value from it. I wish more books had disclaimers like this because it would have not only saved me time but dramatically sped up my growth process. When I was immersed in reading, sometimes covering between 1-4 books a week, I would find myself reading in a passive state. What I mean by this is that I wouldn't actively engage in the tools that these books would teach me. If the book described an exercise for me to do I'd find that 90% of the time I wouldn't complete it. Although I logically understood the concept, I wasn't emotionally invested. And that's the difference between life and death. Think about it... whenever you see a smoker buying a pack of cigarettes from a shop there's a very good chance they can read. But what's the first thing in black and white that it says on that packet? 'This cigarette can kill you and harm those around you'. But what happens next? They open the packet and put that cigarette in their mouth. Now this doesn't mean every smoker doesn't care about themselves or their children, it means they have understood that smoking is bad only on a logical level, but not emotionally. If you are understanding the concepts in this book only on a logical level then they're as good as useless. You may say "I get it, this makes sense" but I guarantee the only way you can ever truly understand this is to put this knowledge into action.

Research has shown that if you read this book passively, within 4 weeks you'll be able to recall approximately 10% of the points you found useful. Not because you didn't enjoy it or you don't have a good memory. But as you'll be exposed to so much more stimuli, these helpful points will filter out. If you take part in the exercises that this book provides, simply by being more cognitively involved, the action of writing it down will groove in these points deeper and you'll be able to recall of 30-40% of the parts that actively helped you or interested you. However, by actually applying these principles into your life you'll be able to recall up to 90% of the books value.

Not engaging in these exercises at the beginning technically meant that I was reading 1 book for every 10 I went through. How long would it take you to read 10 books? That's a lot of time and money wasted.

I therefore urge you to become actively engaged within these contents. Highlight the points that resonate with you emotionally and go back to them. I've attached a glossary at the end of this book, so if you find yourself slightly confused in a particular chapter, you can flick to the back and just get the definition. These principles you will learn have helped, saved and transformed many lives. I can't wait for you to experience the same!

<u>SUPERHUMAN</u>

"Our deepest fear isn't that we're inadequate. Our deepest fear is that we're powerful beyond measure. It's our light, not our darkness that most frightens us"

Marianne Williamson

The Happy Caveman

When we think of our lives now in a settled agriculture environment, it's difficult to imagine anything else in human history considering we've been living in an agricultural society for nearly 10,000 years! However, when we look at the full scale of our species existence (homo sapiens), the emergence of our homo lineage dates back 2 million years, and of that, anatomically modern humans date back nearly 200,000 years. So, when we view the full scale of our existence, living in agricultural societies represents only 5% of our collective experience at most when comparing to our time spent in hunter gatherer social groups.

This is a primary point that we're going to keep going back to throughout this course. The entire premise of the Primal Life Method surrounds the fact that right now in this moment you have the body of a caveman. What this means is that your body, even the way that every neuron is wired to transmit electricity when you think, has been made perfectly. It has evolved incredibly over millions of years to survive and reproduce for maximum efficiency within society. We just have to understand that this maximum efficiency is for a society that lived over 10,000 years ago.

It's difficult for anybody to talk about exactly what we were like in prehistory (hunter gatherer nomad), simply because there were no artefacts left behind. How do we know so much about the Romans? Because of all the artefacts left behind: paintings, scripture, architecture, weapons... all these things give us a fantastic map to look into the day to day activity of their lives. But prehistory is a little more difficult. When we're pulling on the ideas of how these ancestors lived and how that differs from us, we're looking at 4 primary sources. We're looking at:

Anthropological Data – based on hunter gatherer nomadic societies today.

The **Human Anatomy and Physiology** – because the way our body has evolved tells us a lot about how our ancestors were.

Primates – our closest living relative. We share 98% of the same DNA as our primate family. We are equally related to chimps as we are bonobos, in fact we're more related to a bonobo and a chimpanzee than an African elephant is to an Indian elephant.

Psychosocial Issues- The issues which are relevant in western society and how that differs in other areas of the world.

It's no secret that in western society, cases of physical and mental disorders are dramatically on the rise. When we compare that to indigenous tribes around the world that's not the case. We know it's not genetics which is swaying these statistics so much. For example: a Japanese person in the USA is more likely to suffer from depression than he would in Japan. What statistics are also telling us about the most common increase of physical and mental illnesses such as back pain, migraines, cancer, high blood pressure, heart issues, is that they're predominantly caused by lifestyle. What this means is that despite living in a technological and economical 'utopia' we are inherently doing something wrong and these mental and physical illnesses are side effects of these lifestyle choices. Throughout the book I'll be referring to these lifestyle choices as evolutionary mismatches.

If we go back to early man and early woman 14,000+ years ago both would get very definitive rewards/very distinct feelings whenever they carried out certain evolutionary processes. They would get a feeling, a reward, whenever they successfully hunted and gathered and supported their families. We work better as a tribe than we do individually so they also got a feeling anytime they interacted with each other. This feeling that they got, they most definitely recognised. And scientists are adamant about this. Not only did it make them happier and healthier, above all it was a coping mechanism. It helped them cope with the everyday stresses of life. It even helped them cope with physical pain. It made them braver and stronger. This feeling sounds incredible, doesn't it? But now we know that this feeling, this reward they got, wasn't just some abstract concept or some esoteric idea. It was a neurotransmitter that gets released in 3 places: the brain, the heart and the gut. The neurotransmitter that you may have heard of, simply because it's the most important, is serotonin. When we're releasing steady flows of serotonin throughout our body it acts as a biochemical catalyst for that mentally healthy behaviour. When we're releasing serotonin we become happier, healthier and stronger individuals. But if we're feeling depressed and anxious, we've stopped releasing those neurotransmitters. When we are depressed we're barely releasing any serotonin at all. This is why when people suffer from depression, they don't just say that they feel extremely low, much of the time they feel numb! And when we are anxious we're releasing strong spikes of stress hormones like cortisol and adrenaline. We know that if we want to start feeling like the healthy and happy cavemen that we can all be, we need to be releasing more of these neurotransmitters like serotonin, dopamine and oxytocin.

Now... this doesn't mean that you and I need to grab a spear and go live in the wild to get this feeling! But it does mean that there are certain evolutionary parameters that we must live in for that feeling to become second nature. What's the main reason that depression and anxiety have increased so much over the last several years? It's that we've started to move further and further away from the purpose that our genes were given. Depression and anxiety, even obesity and the increase in other diseases, are all symptoms of these evolutionary mismatches.

The best way to remember it is this: if there's something in your mind and body that's not feeling right, it means you have strayed away from the evolutionary parameters that your body was expecting you to live in. The further away you stray, the worse you feel. The moment you move back within those evolutionary parameters. Your biochemistry (cocktail of neurotransmitters and hormones) begins to release and absorb in a way that allows you to thrive. Essentially you become what we refer to as being biochemically sober.

The Biochemical Superhuman

When we start to become biochemically sober it can feel incredible. With increased energy, mental clarity, positive outlook and an abundant level of joy with a background of tranquillity, who wouldn't feel great? I'd go as far to say you feel superhuman. But the truth is, you're not. We're simply acting human. The reason we don't feel so great is because for the last month, year or decade, most of us have been living outside of these evolutionary parameters, changing the rate at which we release these neurotransmitters and making us feel sub-human.

Have you ever watched the movie Limitless? The one where Bradley Cooper plays a writer stuck at rock-bottom, struggling with his relationships, his career, his physical health, even just keeping his apartment clean… but then he comes across a pill which once taken activates every part of the brain and everything changes for him. He now finds the energy to get stuff done with ease, his confidence increases, he has more clarity in every moment and he starts to take advantage of the abundance of opportunities around him.

I'm sure we'd all love a pill that gives us those effects. However sadly life isn't as easy as that. But when people utilise The Primal Life Method extraordinary things happen. It gives me so much fulfilment every single day because I'm constantly being told by people who use the method how limitless they feel, that they're high on life, some people have literally told me that they feel that they've taken some sort of drug!

I remember going from losing my breath when climbing up the stairs to being able to run for hours, feeling like I'd just started and feeling extraordinary at the end of it. But all I was really doing was following the evolutionary parameters that my body had evolved over 200,000 years ago to expect. Being able to be fulfilled and calm in the most hectic of moments, climbing sub-zero degree mountains wearing only shorts and even doing things like holding my breath for 5 minutes seemed like impossible feats for a person. Yet they all now seem second nature. I'm proud of those things, but they're not unique to me. It's been my pleasure time and time again to see people utilise the processes I'm going to take you through and watch them redefine what it means to be human.

In the fast-paced environment that we live in, when it comes to issues regarding our health and overall happiness we've begun to disregard the source and only tackle the symptoms. This can benefit us short-term but in the long-term only make it worse. If you think about it, doing it this way is completely illogical.

If you saw an alcoholic staggering side to side trying to walk up a hill one symptom he'd be expressing is stumbling. What's the best way to help this man? It would be to get him sober. By getting him permanently sober and tackling the source, the symptom of him staggering would vanish just as a by-product of this change. In a society that treats symptoms, instead of getting this man sober it would be the same as me looking at him and thinking 'oh that man is stumbling sideways, I should get him some crutches'. In the short-term that would work great and help him get up the hill in a straight line but we have a problem - he's still drunk. The source of the issue hasn't been tackled.

Let's take this a step further. What if the alcoholic wanted to make serious changes in his life and get a new job, work on his finances, his emotional wellbeing? An incredible step, right? He's got the will to make it work. He could make a new CV, he could join a gym, he could try to meditate, but guess what… he's drunk. No matter how powerful those actions are, by him not being sober the power of his actions are not even a third of how effective they could be.

The same rule applies to us. So often we believe that the sources of our problems come from outside of us. Maybe we are with the wrong partner, maybe we are in the wrong job, perhaps we have the wrong car or house. But like the alcoholic, we're not focusing on the first necessary step which is 'Am I sober?'. Because if the healthy neurotransmitters like serotonin, dopamine and oxytocin aren't being fired in a way that allows that optimal mentally healthy behaviour, then no matter what situation we're in, we won't be able to think clearly and we are going to be feeling awful and nothing is going to feel right.

Becoming biochemically sober won't make you a millionaire. It won't find you the perfect partner, or get you the job of your dreams. But it's the first essential step to getting there. This is because we're starting by tackling the source, not the symptoms. We're seeing life through a clearer filter as opposed to one that is blurred and negative. A great start to a healthier life!

What Is Health?

What is health? It's such a broad term that not one person has the monopoly on. We have health experts, doctors, surgeons, alternative therapists, who all use the word 'health' in every other sentence. Yet when it comes to defining that term we may all have different descriptions. We use the term health within the Primal Life Method and my favourite explanation for health was by Dorian "Doc" Paskowitz. If you who don't know him, look him up; he became very famous as the physician who gave up practising medicine to become a surfing legend. In this process he became world renowned for becoming a health expert. His definition of health was the following: 'health is a state of superior wellbeing, a vigour, a vitality, a pizazz that has to be worked on for every single day of your life'. What this means is that health should be seen as a vehicle and not a destination.

When we're talking about the health of a person what we're not talking about is their fitness level. Fitness and health are not the same, and very often people don't realise how wide the gap is. Fitness is simply defined by someone's athletic activity and their ability to perform physical feats, whether that's in strength, endurance, or both. However, a fit person isn't necessarily healthy. It is fairer to determine health by how optimal the state of someone's body, such as our muscles, our skeletal frame and our hormonal, digestive, lymphatic and nervous systems are operating.

If we wish to go even more microscopic in our health definition, we would determine this by how nourished our cells are. Our cells are the source of all energy in our body. Because cells too are living organisms they need to be oxygenated, hydrated and have very little waste in order to survive and drive the processes in the body; such as respiration, digestion, absorption and detoxification.

Alongside this, it would also involve the absence of disease and infection. But what is disease? What is the source of sickness? The definition can simply be put as the accumulation of toxins in our blood stream.

Our body has evolved to hold a numerous level of functional and efficient methods to eliminate toxins from our bowels, lungs and even our skin. If we're taking in more toxins than our body can eliminate our bodies slowly begin to drain of its life source. Disease however is simply our bodies attempt to cure itself - disease is the cure. When we have a runny nose, we're vomiting or we have diarrhoea this isn't directly the toxins doing this. It's our body using excess energy in a dramatic attempt to eliminate the toxins quicker. However, this takes away optimal activity of our other bodily functions.

Nature Vs Nurture

When it comes to nature and nurture many people believe they are trapped by the DNA they are given. However, more and more research is proving that the choices we make don't just alter us physically, they can alter us on a genetic level as well. Nature of course can play a huge role in the life that we lead, however more and more evidence shows that our lifestyle is becoming a bigger and more effective player in the overall quality of our lives. DNA is not static. We have 20,000 genes in the body which are all just descriptions of proteins with different jobs. There are genes which are associated with higher or lower risk of disease, hormone regulation, vitamin metabolism, physiology, behaviour, sugar preferences, anxiety, and even happiness has a genetic input. To some extent the genes we have been given are irrelevant and what really matters is whether those genes are turned on or off. In an ideal world we want to turn on the genes that are associated with lower risk of disease, and turn off those which could contribute to making us ill. Here's the exciting thing: by changing elements of our lifestyle, we actually have the ability to turn those genes on and off.

There have been experiments with people who feel alone and unhappy. Researchers found that over 209 genes associated with elementary functions of life, like their hormones and metabolism, had changed. What this means is that when we're actively being happy, we can also change those genes. This hasn't just been found in humans, it's been found in other animals as well. Rats, just like humans, are incredibly social. Within female rates there's a gene which can be associated with a strain of breast cancer which resides in about 20% of the female rat population. The moment groups of rats were placed in isolation, that immediately went up to 80% and tumour growth could be detected as being 84x bigger, and the breast cancer began to metastasise – meaning it started to spread to other parts of the body. What an incredible example, simply by doing nothing but changing an environmental factor it caused particular genes to turn on and off, and in this case cause the health of rats to rapidly deteriorate. By knowing this, it's now our choice to follow the right environmental actions that can rapidly increase our health, even to a genetic level, so our bodies can thrive.

Truly understanding the power of epigenetics we have to understand our destiny (even down to the core of our nature) has not yet been carved into stone. There are so many potential versions of ourselves genetically. Following the Primal Life Method will show you some key ways to shift your genetic identity to the one that you want as opposed to settling for the one you believe you were given.

SUPERHUMAN Chapter Summary

- What we feel is what our biochemistry is doing.
- Our biochemistry is a series of chemical processes within our bodies, including the release of neurotransmitters and hormones like serotonin, oxytocin and dopamine.
- When we release serotonin, oxytocin and dopamine we feel happier, more energetic and connected to others. We refer to this as being Biochemically Sober.
- We have the bodies of cavemen and our bodies have been used to a particular type of lifestyle that worked in conjunction with being Biochemically Sober. We don't need to mimic this caveman lifestyle to get the same benefits, but there are parameters we must work in (principles we can follow) that allows us to enjoy the best of both worlds – we can be cavemen in the 21st century.
- When we're suffering mentally and/or physically and develop lifestyle-based illnesses it is because we have moved away from the evolutionary parameters that our genes have adapted for. This is called evolutionary mismatches.
- The Primal Life Method are those principles/parameters.
- In order for us to successfully change, the best starting point is threshold. Threshold is when you're in a position where you feel something must change, that something is you, and it has to happen now. Threshold and rock-bottom are not the same thing, however they can occur at the same time.

- Our DNA is not static. We all have unique sets of genes, however it's whether those genes are expressed (turned on or off) that will make a difference to our health. By changing environmental factors like our actions we have the ability to turn on/off those genes – following the Primal Life principles can do this.

THINK

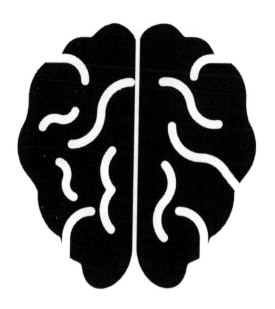

"I am what I think about all day long. Once you realise this you start to become real careful what you think about"

Wayne Dyer

How The Brain Works

It's no secret that the way we think can determine the way we can feel. Something even as simple as a thought can completely change spikes of hormones which are released throughout our body. However, as you'll soon learn throughout this book other processes which change the hormones in our body will completely change the way we think – it's a bi-directional process. But for us to understand how we think, why we think in the patterns we do, even why we're caught in a negative loop and can't get out, it's vital we understand how the brain works.

To begin looking at how the brain works, let's start with what causes depression and anxiety, and even things like OCD and stress, but more importantly what we can do about it.

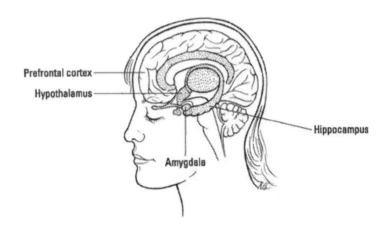

The pre-frontal cortex is the part of the brain you would recognise as you. It's the part of you that's consciously reading this right now. It's the part that allows you to be aware of our interactions and interact with the world around us. At the moment this is attached to a vast intellectual resource, which in this book we refer to as the intellectual mind (frontal lobe).

When we operate from this part of the brain we tend to be more successful in our actions. One of the reasons being that this part of the brain comes up with a proper assessment of this situation and is generally very positive. This is a part of the brain we don't tend to share with animals. But there is another part of the brain. A part which we will refer to as the emotional mind (limbic system). The centre and most influential parts is known as the amygdala or the fight, flight, depression area of the brain. It's attached to two other primitive parts of the brain. We have the hippocampus which is responsible for all our primitive and sometimes inappropriate behavioural patterns and responses, and the hypothalamus which regulates all the chemicals in the body and mind. Let's say that after this chapter you close the book, turn around, and there's a sabre tooth tiger standing there. What do you think would happen? You'd move suddenly from the intellectual mind straight into the emotional mind. Your heart beat would start racing, your palms would start to sweat, your stomach would do that horrible churning feeling, and you'd be off like a shot.

Now you'll be pleased to know that in this circumstance that would be an entirely appropriate response. Unfortunately we can still get the same response in modern day living, like when our financial sources are being threatened, when we're having an argument with someone important to us, or if we don't think we fit in. When our anxiety goes up (and it can be a gradual process) the emotional mind will actually hijack the brain and we move from the intellectual mind and become dominated by the emotional part. The emotional mind normally works within 3 parameters: depression, anxiety and anger. Or if we're really unlucky, sometimes a combination of all three.

If for some reason or another the emotional part of the brain thinks you're in some kind of danger it will step into help. Depression, anxiety and danger are actually just primitive opt-out clauses.

If we go back 14,000 years when the caveman would look outside of his cave and there was snow or ice or danger... he would go back into his cave, he'd pull the rug over his head, and he wouldn't interact with anyone or anything until the situation had changed and it was safe to go back out. His metabolism would start to slow down, his energy would conserve itself, and he'd go into a soft hibernation mode. You can see how we've fitted this into modern day symptoms of depression. If we're suffering from depression, generally our energy is going to be low; in fact in most cases of depressed people, they will feel fatigued most of the time. If we were in the jungle in those days, you can doubt very much that we'd be too far away from our panic buttons at any given time. Anger is just a primitive way of increasing our strength to defend ourselves against wild animals and other tribesmen.

The emotional mind has a few other qualities. One of which is it's very negative. When we are operating in the emotional mind, we are wired to see things from a worst-case scenario. And if you think about it, it kind of has to for your self-preservation. If you turned around now and the sabre tooth tiger was there, you wouldn't want to think 'oh it's ok, it's past dinner time so he's probably already eaten'. Quite rightly you'd want to think of the worst thing that could happen, which in this case would be 'run, this thing is going to eat me'. It's this kind of negative thinking that helped our DNA survive for the last 200,000 years.

Remember, the emotional mind doesn't care about whether you're happy or not, that's your job. It only cares about whether we're surviving. Another quality that it has is that it's obsessive. If that sabre tooth tiger were to follow you home or everywhere you went, this part of the brain would remind you of it constantly. Every 5 minutes you would be reminded to keep checking your window to see if it's outside; you can see how an extreme version of this could lead to OCD type tendencies. I bet right now that if a negative thought comes into your head you don't think about it just once, do you? You think about it 50 times, running in a negative loop, one which you sometimes feel you can't get out of!

Another quality is that it's vigilant. If for some reason or another the emotional mind thinks that there's danger around then it would be wise to stay on red alert. And because this part of the brain isn't innovative and can't come up with new ideas, it will always rely on previous patterns of behaviour. If what we did yesterday ensured our survival, this part of the brain would encourage us to do it again. If yesterday you stayed in bed and didn't interact with anyone and felt miserable, this part of your brain the next day would want you to do this again. Of course you weren't happy, but you survived, didn't you? So the limbic system/emotional mind believes it's doing its job.

What causes us to move from the happy logical part of our mind to the depressed, anxious and angry part when there's no danger around? In short, it's caused by negative thinking. It's not necessarily the events in life which cause that feeling of crisis for us, but the perception/meaning of that event instead. If it was just the event which caused the feeling of depression or anxiety then every single student would have a panic attack. Every single surgeon who had a bad operation would never be able to go in the next day. And we know that's not the case, don't we? We know it comes down to the individual thought patterns surrounding that event itself, it can be the big things like

'I'm never going to be able to afford my rent'

'I'm never going to be able to overcome this obstacle'

'I'm never going to find a partner'

But it can just as easily be the small things too. Such as 'that meeting', 'that social event', 'that conversation you need to have'. Now this is an important time to say that the emotional mind can't determine the difference between reality and your imagination. Logically and intellectually, you know that event is going to go great. You've done it before, you can do it again. But when you're locked in the emotional mind you start to picture things going wrong. You think about it 50 times or possibly more, perhaps even losing sleep over it. Now when it comes to that event taking place and it goes absolutely fine, (intellectually you knew it would). But remember, the emotional mind hasn't gone to one event... it's gone to 51. One event, the real one, went great, but fifty imagined events were total disasters! Not a fair ratio is it, so the next time you have to do this you can only guess how you'll feel again.

It's peculiar when we take a moment to think about it, that we have the ability to worry and in extreme cases have a full-blown panic attack about something that's not even happening. If you're human I'm sure you've been worried about something happening the next day. Now the reality of the situation is that tomorrow doesn't exist. As much as we believe we are, we are not clairvoyant... we cannot tell the future. The only real thing in our life is right here and right now. We also have the ability to retrospect negatively about the past. But again, the best thing about the past is that it's already happened. When people feel depressed, generally but not always, it's about something in the past. If they feel anxious it's normally about something in the future.

The Stress Bucket

Every negative thought we have is stored and accumulated. I like to say it's stored in a stress bucket. Now I'm sure you've had it when little stresses have built up and built up, and then it only took the tiniest thing, the straw which broke the camel's back, to make the bucket overflow.

Did you ever see the movie Splash with Tom Hanks? There's a scene at the beginning where he is an Usher for a wedding and earlier that afternoon his long-term girlfriend has broken up with him. Every single person who comes into the church says "hey, great to see you, how's Victoria?" to which he replies "Oh, she's ill, she can't make it". He continues to talk to his brother about the breakup, feeling a little bit worried. Suddenly more guests walk past and again ask "hey, great to see you, how's Victoria?". To which he says "Flu, sadly. Couldn't make it, maybe next time". And as this continues to go on for a few minutes, obviously he's becoming more stressed each time, to the point where the groom walks past and says "Hi Alan" to which Tom Hanks suddenly snaps and screams "SHE LEFT ME, OK… SHE'S NOT COMING. YOU'VE GOT THE NEWS, NOW DO YOU WANT THE WEATHER?!".

We've all had times like that, but what's happening in those moments? The secret lies in something called cortisol, the primary hormone that's released during stress. In acute doses cortisol can actually be quite good for us. Whenever you see a rabbit being chased by a predator, and it's running for its life… in that moment the rabbit, or any sort of prey, will get a huge spike of cortisol. That cortisol will help optimise the prey's body in its performance so it can survive. But what happens after the rabbit successfully escapes? It will shake itself off, release any of the trapped cortisol in its body, and the stress in its life stops - it returns to the present moment. As humans (due to negative thinking) we have the ability to replay that stressful event over and over and eventually, we build up chronic levels of cortisol. And we can physically feel that, can't we? I'm sure after a long day at the office, if it's been stressful you can feel that tension in the tops of your shoulders and the bottom of your back. Even though you've most likely been sitting at a desk or doing something very sedentary, your body has spent the last several hours in a chronic state of fight or flight. It's during chronic levels of cortisol that our body starts to break down.

Now, what is severe stress? It's a chronic level of cortisol. Not only is this stress hormone at consistently high levels, it is the number one immuno-depressant, nothing on this planet will be able to get you more ill than high levels of cortisol – and it's also the number one aging hormone. Now we know biologically why people suffering from stress can get sick and also why we can see it in their faces.

Thankfully as you go through this book I'm going to teach you how to empty that stress bucket. My personal aim throughout these chapters and my wish to you is that you can wake up every morning with a completely empty bucket.

Our Map Of The World

We have approximately 60,000 thoughts in a day, and 80% of those will be identical to the thoughts we had yesterday. When we're thinking, what's actually happening? We're firing neurons.

Currently your brain has 100 billion neurons. Just to give that number a bit more perspective, you have the same amount of neurons in your brain than there are stars in the galaxy. A neuron is a brain cell that receives processes and then transmits electrical and chemical signals. When we're thinking, what's really happening is a series of neurons (a neural network) are firing these electrical impulses through our brain. A cool way of phrasing it is that our neural network is the currency of our reality.

When we're looking at an object, light will hit that object, an image gets reflected into our retina which can only filter visible light and our brains produce a series of neural networks so within a split second, an image is presented to us. The exact same thing can be said for sound – 2 objects collide, sound waves travel throughout the air, (and all sound waves are vibrations) these vibrations travel through the ear canal... the brain's currency gets to work and that becomes a noise, a voice, a word, that produces an algorithm we recognise. So, to simplify what do we mean? It means that life isn't happening out there... it's actually happening inside our heads.

A wonderful example of how neural networks can be different is in a condition that some people are born with called synaesthesia – this is a case where our currency is different to the average person. So instead of just hearing a sound, that person might see a colour. In effect, it means they're hearing through colours. When they're spelling out a word, as opposed to visualising letters they might be able to taste that word. The quality of our lives, the quality of our reality, is really the quality of our neural networks.

It shows us that there is no distinct relationship between an event and a person, it's our representation of the event that causes the relationship. Another way to present this is that good or bad things don't happen.... they don't exist... it's the meaning we give those events that make them good or bad.

One of my favourite stories is a case study of two genetically identical twins who had a drunk and violent father. One of the boys grew up to become a drug addict and eventually went to prison. The other had a very successful life with a good job and a great family life. When they were asked the cause of why they turned out the way they did, the most fascinating element is that they gave the same response: "My father was a drunk and violent to me. Can you blame me?".

Isn't that amazing? That two people with the same genetics, experiencing the same event, can have two very different futures simply because of the interpretation of it. Because they gave that event different meanings, it shaped their destiny in two very different ways. One gave the meaning that this is how people are and this is how life will be but the other one said "I will never be anything like the way this man is".

Take a second to think about a few moments in your life. I'm sure there's something that you went through in the past that at the time seemed would have seemed negative; perhaps you were being bullied, had an embarrassing moment, a traumatic experience, or maybe something smaller like a mild discomfort. At the time you believed this to be the worst thing that could happen to you, but when you look back on it now you realise that in its own crazy way, it was a gift.

I remember one of my clients. She grew up with a verbally abusive mother. This lady grew up in a very close-minded household where having views which were different from the norm would be shut down, she'd be insulted and laughed at. She was telling me how one weekend she couldn't wait to take her 4 and 6 year olds to a gay pride event. She told me that she just couldn't wait for her children to understand that no matter what sexual orientation someone is, that they are no different to them. She wanted to embed in them the core value that all people are equal, and that meant so much to her. It slowly dawned on her that if she had gotten the mother she always wanted - then she wouldn't be the mother that she's proud to call herself today. And suddenly growing up in a close-minded household was one of the best gifts she'd ever been given. It allowed her to look back on her childhood and experience true gratitude. This just goes to show that actually in all those decades, the events never changed did they? The meaning she gave those events changed. The idea of that memory was represented…. it was RE-presented to her in a different way, through a different filter, that now empowered her. The representation of that memory had changed.

It just goes to show us that reality is never set. The way we view the world is simply a map, not the territory. It's a scary thought. But what makes this so exciting is that if you're not happy with your map of the world, you can change it. The same thing goes for good feelings as well, doesn't it? If you ever have the privilege to buy a new car, let's say it's the car you've always dreamed of, chances are you're going to feel great… for a while. But who gives you that feeling? It's not the car. It's just the same when people have lots of money. We don't feel more relaxed, comfortable or ecstatic just because we have more pieces of paper with a face on it. We feel ecstatic because of the meaning we give that car, the meaning we give those pieces of paper and more importantly, the feeling we believe we're going to get from it. No-one gives you that feeling but you.

Do you remember your first kiss? I remember the first kiss with my partner, I practically flew home. I was swinging off lampposts like Gene Kelly, jumping in puddles and stopping traffic. But again, as romantic as that might be, it wasn't the kiss that did that. It was my thought pattern thinking this girl liked me, and how much I liked her. Just by thinking those things I was able to dramatically change my biochemistry and release those sparks of neurotransmitters throughout my body. It wasn't wet tissue touching wet tissue which did that. If that was the case I would get the same feeling every time I kissed my Grandma. As lovely as she is, I can assure you I don't.

The message that "the meaning we give events shapes our reality, not the other way around" seems to be universal in most teachings whether it's neuroscience, self-development, psychology and even in older spiritual practises like Buddhism and Taoism.

Because it's so important, this idea will continue to be a running theme throughout this chapter. Once we understand this, and think within the parameters that our map is not the territory - our bad days become non-existent, our bad moments become minimal, and we're one step closer to living that happier and healthier life that we all have available to us.

Neuroplasticity

Every year we are learning more and more about the brain and the findings just from the last several years have been incredible. If there's one word I want you to remember from this chapter, it's neuroplasticity. I'll say that again. Neuroplasticity. It means that our brain is more like play-doh than it is porcelain. It is the scientific proof that our identity, our beliefs, the way we perceive reality, the way we engage with the world around us, is in a constant state of flux. So, what does this mean for us? When we're thinking positively and feeling great, we can see on functional brain scans that the pre-left frontal cortex lights up.

There have been studies done with groups of Tibetan Monks and something that was practically universal between them was that they had larger or technically more activated pre-left frontal cortices. A neuroscientist called Richard Davidson studied this further to answer the questions 'do you need to be enlightened?' 'do you need to have the same peace and tranquillity as a Tibetan Monk for a pre-left frontal cortex to be this activated?' 'Is this something the Tibetan Monks were just born with?'. He took a group of volunteers and for 12 weeks he got them to use a variety of mental tools. At the end of the experiment, all the participants described themselves as feeling more positive and overall more grateful. And then when they looked at their brain scans they could see that all their pre-left frontal cortices had grown (become more active)! Isn't that incredible? Just like a bodybuilder sculpts his body to grow certain muscles and become physically stronger - every single one of us as humans have the ability to sculpt our minds.

I want to do an experiment with you. Get a pen and paper, writing journal, or use your phone, and take as long as you need to list all the emotions you experience within the average week.

Ok, did you do it? Remember what I said at the beginning of this book… it's only through actively doing these exercises that you're going to understand this on an emotional level. So take some more time and see if you can push a few more emotions!

In the English language there's hundreds of words to describe the way we're feeling. I don't know how long you spent on this task, but your list is probably not close to 100! Do you have 100? I imagine you haven't. What about 50? Actually, what about 20? No I'm going to bet you're going to have around 12 emotions on there. Now that's crazy when you think about it. Throughout a whole week, 168 hours, you only experience approximately 12 emotions… and half of those make you feel like crap. But all of us will have a natural state, a natural thought-pattern which we will run with throughout the day.

When we look at an image of our brain it looks like this soft white organ. The reason brain matter looks white is reported because of the numerous amount of myelinated neurons. When we've used a particular neural network over and over again a process called myelination starts to occur. Myelin is often compared to the plastic insulation over a copper wire – it insulates the neuron so that the electric impulse can travel faster. The average impulse in the body will travel at around 5 metres per second, but the moment it has a myelinated sheath around it some impulses can go as fast as 100 meters per second. This is where it gets interesting though; the more you do a particular action, the more myelinated that neuron becomes, the signal travels faster and the action becomes easier to perform.

Can you guess where this is going? Woolaa, a habit is formed! We hear quotes all the time that repetition is the mother of all skill. One of my favourite quotes of all time is from Aristotle – "We are what we repeatedly do. Excellence therefore is not an act, but a habit". Our brains can prove it. However it isn't through making one change temporarily in our thought-pattern that changes our reality. Not for long anyway. We have to myelinate those neural pathways and that takes lots of repetition. If you imagine a snow-covered mountain and you have all these snowboarders trying to get down the mountain, what happens to the first snowboarder? He will be the slowest because he has to struggle in forming his own path. The second snowboarder will follow the track and perhaps find a slightly different path, still struggling, but it's slightly easier thanks to the first snowboarder's tracks. As each new snowboarder goes down the mountain they'll get faster and the ride will be easier. A phrase that sums this up is 'neurons that fire together, wire together'.

Another phrase you're going to hear time and time again, not just in this book but when it comes to the subject of health, is 'if you don't use it, you lose it'. Over the course of a few weeks and months, what would happen to the quality of the track that the snowboarders made if they stopped riding it? It would disappear – it would become snowed over.

However even if it didn't get snowed over, the quality of the track could be affected another way. If the snowboarders decided to make a completely new pathway down the mountain, and if they were to do this repeatedly they would eventually make a deeper and faster track. So much so that when new snowboarders came to the mountain and had to find the quickest way down they would take the most used pathway.

Thoughts have a similar process. If we want to experience a particular emotion or thought that's different to the original emotions we wrote down, just like the snowboarders we're going to have to make a new pathway. But in our case a neural pathway, one we're going to have to repeat and strengthen – because remember, we are what we **repeatedly** do.

I remember when I was first learning to drive. I don't know about you, but I thought it was terrifying. Here I was in a big metal outfit (basically the description of Robocop) with the ability to sprint at 80 miles per hour. To make matters worse I'd be on roads that were surrounded by hundreds of other Robocops – scary times. When learning manual/stick shift I could see there were 3 peddles and I had 2 feet... in my mind the math already wasn't adding up! I had to be able to see the 360 degree view around me at all times, and I was being told by the instructor that I would have to get from A to B without killing someone... or dying for that matter! You can only imagine what a mess I was the first time out. But what happened? Even though the sensation of driving was alien to me at first, by continuing to repeat particular actions – checking my rear-view mirror, looking at the lights, hitting the correct pedals at the right time – all of this after many hours of deliberate practice became second nature. My identity in that moment went from somebody learning to drive to becoming a driver. When we're doing anything new it's obviously going to feel alien at first and I think driving is such a great example of that. Now we have millions of people around the world (all dressed as Robocop) who would have had a similar feeling when starting – the same nerves, the same anxiety. You'll now see those exact same people chatting to passengers or singing along to the radio while driving - they're not even consciously thinking about how to drive a car!

That's the primary point that we're looking to explore in this chapter. We're going to learn to stretch the way we're thinking, strengthen the neural pathways we want, and lose the ones which have been holding us back.

Focus

When we're looking to make any change or transformation in our life, whether that's a transformation in our body or biochemistry, improving our health, whether that's progressing in our mission or career, we must have an outcome, something to move towards. We must first have a defined idea of what we want.

But the issue which most of us have before starting a journey like this is figuring out what we want. If we've been caught in a negative loop, and have been stuck in the limbic system; if we're focused on simply avoiding pain, then all we really get a sense of is what we don't want. When people come to see me in my clinic, the first question I'll ask is "How can I help?". 9 times out of 10 if someone is suffering within the parameters of the stresses I've mentioned like depression, anxiety or anger, they'll usually start by telling me what they don't want.

As a side note, you don't need to be suffering from depression, anxiety or anger to be experiencing symptoms. If we're feeling like we're lacking serious motivation and we want to go into hibernation mode this is a mild symptom of depression, but it doesn't mean you are depressed! If we're feeling worried about something that's happening in the future, like a house move or a career change, it doesn't mean we're suffering from severe anxiety, but we're working within the parameter of anxiety. If we're feeling annoyed towards a friend it doesn't mean we're suffering from rage issues, it just means we're working in the parameter of anger. It's the depth you work within that parameter which causes the severity of that condition.

When someone is working within those parameters and they're not seeing things through the left frontal cortex, they'll tell me what they don't want.

They don't want to be depressed anymore

They don't want to have panic attacks

They don't want to feel stressed at work

They don't want to be overweight

The issue we have when we phrase a goal in the negative is that we have absolutely nothing to work towards. "Not being depressed" isn't an emotion, "not being obese" isn't a weight category. Think about this example:

If you were to stand in a dark room blindfolded and I expected you to hit bullseye on a dartboard, (you had no idea where the dartboard was) and I said "Ok, I want you to hit the bullseye, but just to help you out I can tell you it's not on the back of the door". What are the chances of you hitting that target? It's going to be close to zero isn't it? The only way you're going to hit that bullseye is if you're extremely lucky, it would almost be an accident. But, if I told you that I'd hung the dartboard to your left, in the centre of the wall, the chances of you hitting that bullseye suddenly goes up exponentially.

The first step we need to make whenever we're looking to grow is to find what we want to grow towards as opposed to where we're trying to move away from. A wonderful example of this is my college friend James who had won a Mercedes experience for a day at one of their racetracks. He got to spend the day driving their cars. As practise to test his car control, they put him in something called a spin car. A spin car is a vehicle with a frightening twist, while you're sitting at the wheel, the instructor sits in the passenger seat and has access to 4 buttons. Whenever he pushes each of those 4 buttons it allows for one of the wheels to come off the ground and causes the car to spin in a particular direction. Professional race car drivers use this as a way to practice getting control of the car if it starts to slide off course. Before they went around the track the instructor said to James "James, the most common mistake people make is when their car or motorbike starts to slide out of control, they look in the direction of where that vehicle is moving, as opposed to looking where they want to go". He said "Whatever you're looking at in the car, your hands subconsciously start to steer in that direction".

This made a lot of sense to me. How often is it that you hear a story when a car has crashed into a field and there was nothing 100 meters to the left, nothing 100 meters to the right, and the car hit the tree or post in the middle of the field? Why? Because the driver was looking at where he didn't want to go. 'I don't want to hit that tree, I don't want to hit that tree, I don't want to hit that tree'.

The instructor said to James "When you're least expecting it, the car is going to lose control and it's your job to look back to the road to gain control of the vehicle again".

So off they went. James put his foot flats down on the floor, he was mindfully keeping his eye on the instructor wondering at which bend he'd push the button on. But of course the instructor knew when he was looking. The moment James relaxed, BANG, that's when the instructor hit the button, and low and behold the car started to veer off into a spin, and they were sliding towards a wall. So, what did James do in that instant? He looked at the wall!!! I remember saying "Why did you do that?", he replied "I wanted to see where I was going to die". But the instructor knowing that he would do this instinctively pushed James's face away from the wall and to the road. At first James was resisting because as he said, his death was just over "there" (the direction of the wall). But eventually, as his face was being forced to focus on the road he subconsciously started to steer towards it. Finally, the wheels caught their grip and they were able to get back on the track.

They parked up and the instructor said "James, what did I tell you?" and James said "I know, I know, I shouldn't look at the wall, but it was instinctual".

The second time they went around the track, James had his eye on the corner that they had lost control first time, but the instructor didn't push the button there. However like the first time, the moment James relaxed BANG the car went off the road and he lost control of the car. But what did James do this time? He looked at the wall again, didn't he?! So again the instructor pushed his face, but quicker this time James was able to get focused on the road and take control of the car.

This happened a few times, but eventually James created the habit… they'd slide off course left or right but James wouldn't take his eyes off where he wanted to go.

It's incredible isn't it? Just how powerful focus is in those settings. But here's an interesting question, if the car lost control and they were moving towards the wall and James was looking to the road, was he guaranteed not to hit the wall? No. There's no guarantees in life, and sometimes that negative momentum carries us further than we expect. But if, when he lost control, he stared at the wall was he guaranteed to hit it? Absolutely.

Focus is vital in determining the probability of our success. We always need to reframe things in a manner that shows us what we want as opposed to what we don't want.

Just as an experiment to show you how powerful focus really is, I want you to try something right now. The average short-term memory can remember 7 things, plus or minus 2. I want you to take a full 360-degree view of the room you're in and try to remember everything that is red, everything which has the colour red on it. When you're ready, remember the names of everything red. Stand up…. Take a look. Turn around slowly, anything that's red…. Anything which could resemble red. Ok, keep turning. Fantastic. Got all those in your mind? Now keeping your eyes fixed intently on the page, I want you to re-call everything you saw, which was….GREEN!

That is not a typo, try to recall everything that's green. But I want you to keep your eyes focused on the page so the room is not in your peripheral vision – no cheating! remember everything green. When I do this with most people, they can barely remember a thing. And if they do re-call one or two items, it's usually a guess they get wrong or a logical guess – like remembering a plant in the room and assuming it would have to be green. However, they wouldn't be recalling it from memory.

OK, so let's do it again. Do the exact same circle…. Don't move anything, everything stays exactly how it was. Now, look for green. This isn't a trick, genuinely look for green this time. Keep turning

….

And stare into the page.

Did you see more green that time? Of course you did. Why? Because you were looking for it.

There's a particular part of the brain called the reticular activating system. This cleverly filters all your sensory information, all the things that are happening around you, all the sensations, the sights and sounds, even the thoughts to your conscious mind. Your conscious mind can only really focus on 7 things at a time. The best way I had it described to me is if you went into the attic to see everything you'd stored over the years, and all you had with you was a flashlight, the moment you pop the flashlight on, you can only see 7 items in that light. When you move the flashlight from one side of the room to the other, those 7 items are no longer in your view and the new 7 items are. A perfect example is you probably haven't taken much notice of what sensations are on your feet right now. Well, that is until we consciously decided to focus on it. (you're thinking about it now though aren't you, what did you stop focusing on to think of your feet?)

The exact same thing occurs with emotions. When we're looking for everything that's red, everything that's wrong in life; then all the green stuff, the good stuff - goes straight into our blind spot... and we're no longer taking any notice. It doesn't mean it's not there. It just means that we're not looking for it.

What's wrong is always going to be available. But so is what's right. In the next chapter I'm going to share with you an exercise called the Sparkling Moment. What this is going to do is change the red filters we might currently have on, to a brand new set of green filters.

Here's an interesting note to add...

There's a good chance that when you were looking for what was red in the room, or what was green in the room, you may have focused on things which weren't even red or green. You might have seen something that was maroon, burgundy, orange... but counted it as red so you got more things. Instead of green things you may have seen turquoise or cyan. Which means we can find things, even when they're not there! The same again goes for emotions. If I truly wanted to find a reason to be paranoid about something in my life, I'd be able to find it, even if it wasn't there. Same as if I was scared, angry or upset. But by moving the green filters across my vision, by looking for what's right, it will also allow me to experience gratitude and feel positive about the smallest things that I may not have even thought about before. The good and bad stuff is going to be happening to all of us, which one do you want to focus on? Because we know from neuroplasticity that really is your choice. Time for me to show you....

Sparkling Moment

I first came across this when I was training to become a hypnotherapist several years back. This stood out to me not only because it's a great exercise but also because it had such a camp name! I've had people in the past try to refer to it with different names, such as 'moments of greatness', but I refuse to refer to it as anything but the Sparkling Moment.

Were you ever unfortunate enough to lose multiple hours of your life watching the film Pollyanna? I personally can't stand the film – it consists of an over the top annoyingly happy girl who is bugging all the staff inside a stately home, mainly because they're all so negative while she's so happy-go-lucky. Now I like to think of myself as a positive guy, but Pollyanna was just too much for me. Anyway, part way through the film Pollyanna falls out of a tree and breaks her leg. I was thrilled!!! She had been the most annoying girl I had ever seen on screen. Despite its 2 hour 15min running time, Pollyanna does give us one nugget of gold. She refers to this as the Glad Game. It starts when a few members of the household staff are stuck in a moaning rant – one complains about working on a Sunday, another complains about something else... and Pollyanna suggests playing this game. When asked what it is, she says it's a game her dad taught her for when things aren't going to plan and it makes her feel better. We're going to do something similar now with the Sparkling Moment.

When I talked about neuroplasticity, I mentioned the part of the brain which lights up when we're feeling positive. In neurological terms, unbeknown to Pollyanna, the Glad Game was a way to exercise the left pre-frontal cortex. To create/myelinate a neural pathway that made it easier for her to remember all the good things which have genuinely been happening.

What we're going to do now is recall 10 Sparkling Moments - 10 positive things which have happened over the course of the last week (it's best to write them down). Now what's great is these can all be relevant to you, what a Sparkling Moment is for one person may not be a Sparkling Moment for another. It doesn't need to be huge things like "It was great when I won the lottery this week", it can be the smallest of things too. I remember I had a client who during this exercise recalled that while doing the washing up, he looked out the window and noticed the flowers were blooming. That was a Sparkling Moment for him.

But here's the twist – I'm going to digress momentarily to talk about something called the Training Effect. Remember when I compared body building to sculpting our mind? There's a very specific thing a body builder has to do to gain muscle… If you and I were going to get some weights on our barbell and do 10 bicep curls, which rep do you think would be the one responsible for 90% of the growth? It's the 11th! When we put our muscles under more strain than they can handle at one time, they rip. When they heal back they will over compensate. In short, our muscles are saying 'that was tough, we don't want to rip again, so let's grow back stronger. The next time we do that weight, we won't rip'. But what does the body builder do the next time around? He picks up a heavier weight, pushing himself out of the physical comfort zone, and demanding for the growth to continue.

We're going to do the exact same thing with our brain right now. If you haven't done this exercise recently, it can be hard to find 10 things. At some point during this exercise when you're trying to remember the good things which have happened, you'll come to a block. You'll think there are no other moments, in fact you may even convince yourself of this.

But just like the body builder at this point, we need to push for that 11th rep. The moment we do that, the flood gates open and one, two, five more will pop out!

I remember doing this with one of my clients who was suicidal. He was only able to come up with 2 Sparking Moments, one of which was "I came here today". After he came up with those 2 he looked at me and said "I think I'm scraping the barrel here". He was convinced there were no more positive things. But five minutes later, just by pushing for it, by exercising his pre-left frontal cortex, he had 10!

Simply by doing that exercise, what are we doing? We're strengthening our neural network, myelinating, building those neuropathways to recall positive memories. So much so that if you do this in a week's time it will be easier. That same client only three sessions later was able to recall 10 off the top of his head. Instead of his block being at 2, it was now at 12.

So, just as a forewarning, some of you will be utterly convinced that there are no more. But remember in the section when we looked at the power of focus; if we've been looking through the red filters for so long, of course we're not going to believe there's any green. It's vital we keep pushing so that our left frontal cortex is exercised.

Logical Levels

Here's where we start to go a little bit deeper into the levels of change available to us. I first came across this from Dr Mike Mandel, who is probably one of the most prominent unconscious educators out there, and I believe it was originally created by John Grinder, one of the co-creators of Neuro-Linguistic Programming (NLP).

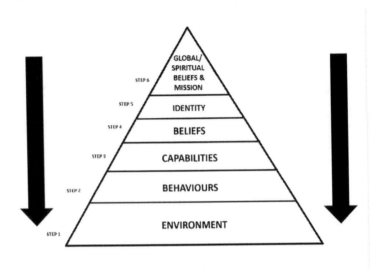

This can usually be shown as a pyramid with 6 logical levels of change. Let's start with the base, which is environment. Many of us, including myself at one time, have believed that our health and happiness was determined by the environment around us.

How many of us in the past have believed that things would just be a bit better if our boss was nicer to us at work, we'd be happier if our children were better behaved, if our partner showed us more affection? The issue with this is that all these things are outside of ourselves.

We can get a temporary uplift in our emotions when those things change. The issue with relying on external circumstances for our happiness is that we have no control over them. If I allow my personal wellbeing to be hung on something outside of myself then my life is going to feel like a rollercoaster. My primary focus is on what I can't control.

If we go back over 2,000 years to a famous group of philosophers called the Stoics such as Marcus Aurelius, Seneca and Epictetus, speaking about living a good life they said that we need to focus on the only 2 things that we can control: our own thoughts and our own actions. It reminds me of a lecture I once saw being done by a Buddhist Monk who was giving a talk on why we never need to worry. He asked a member of the audience "Can someone give me a problem?" and a gentleman gave him one. The Monk wrote the problem in a bubble on the board behind him. He then asked the gentleman "Can you do something about this?" to which the gentleman replied "Yes, I can". He drew a line to another bubble and wrote inside it 'Why worry?'. He then asked for another problem from the audience, to which a lady gave him one and he asked the same question, "Can you do anything about this?". She answered quite confidently "No, I can't. I can't do anything!". The Monk simply drew a line going from her problem to the same bubble and said "So, why worry?".

It's down to us to take control of our own thoughts and actions. Here's an example of wanting our environment to change... Let's say we want our partner to offer us more affection. We need to move up a level to the next logical level of change, which is our behaviours.

In order for us to change our environment, we need to take it so it's under our control which involves changing our own behaviours. For me to change my behaviour I need to start by asking a different question. Instead of asking 'why doesn't my partner give me affection?' I need to ask 'what behaviours am I doing which are supporting the actions they're taking?'. What a great question. Isn't it amazing the moment we ask ourselves a different question surrounding the same subject, we're able to get a completely different answer which we're going to able to use to help us?! Questions are so important that there's an entire section on this later in the book.

What behaviours can I change which will no longer support my partner's actions? Well, if I want more affection I could give more affection. How could I give more affection? I could make her favourite dish, she'd be over the moon with that! Fantastic – we've changed our behaviour and moved towards changing our environment - if we want to. It's trickled down to the bottom level. However we've hit a snag, because our behaviours are limited by our capabilities.

We've got our environment, we know the behaviour we want to change, but the problem is that if I'm not capable of that behaviour, if I don't know how to cook her favourite dish, then I'm limiting the behaviours I can put into place. I need to build my resources so I'm actually capable of putting the behaviour I want into place. But what are our capabilities limited by? Our beliefs.

The first step I need to take in order to build on my resources to widen my capabilities is to believe that it's possible in the first place. If I don't believe that I can cook then I've already restricted my ability to learn the capabilities needed to put into place the behaviours required, which will of course alter the environment. (Have I lost you yet? Don't worry this will make sense!)

Our beliefs are a huge segment in how we think, I've dedicated an entire section to it in this chapter. But there's even something which limits my beliefs and that's my identity, which again has its own dedicated section coming soon.

Identity is a huge driving force in the quality of our life. If in the fibre of my being I don't think I'm a cook, that's just not me and that's not part of my identity, then how on earth am I going to start believing that I can learn that skill and be capable?

At the top of the pyramid, something that I as your coach won't have access to, is your deepest mission/your spiritual beliefs. Let me give some examples here. The moment you change the top of that pyramid, EVERYTHING will be affected in a trickle-down effect. Let's say I want to change my behaviour and I want to stop eating meat. I could work on affecting that behaviour, but if I become a Buddhist and believe that eating meat damages my Karma, you can see that changing that behaviour would be an automatic overnight process.

If I wanted to stop the behaviour of smoking, that's going to be really hard if I identify as a smoker. When people come to see me to stop smoking, I always ensure that even when they're coming in a smoker, they leave a non-smoker as opposed to a smoker who has temporarily stopped smoking.

If you're looking to make a change in your diet like giving up meat or dairy, the moment you identify with being a Vegan, the moment you join Vegan communities, the moment you say "I'm Jane and I'm a Vegan" then your habit of eating meat will disappear as a by-product of that identity change.

Often in the USA when we look at the most radical changes we can see it's all about someone's core mission/beliefs. You can find an example of someone who used to be a member of Hell's Angels and was regularly attacking people with baseball bats. However, after going to prison and becoming a born-again-Christian, what changes in them? Everything!

What we can learn from this pyramid is that if we want to make a change on one of these levels, the most successful and lasting way to do it is to go to one of the previous levels before it.

If I want to change my behaviour I'm best off changing my belief. But if I want to go even deeper then I'll need to look at changing my identity. I'll be teaching you how to do this in more details over the next few sections.

Identity

When we think of identity, we imagine it to be a never-changing entity. Who am I? I'm me. I'll always be me. I always have been me. But we have to remember just like everything else, identity is always fluctuating.

Let's look at this on a biological level. Approximately every month you have an entirely new set of skin cells. Every four months you have entirely new red blood cells. Every year you have entirely new white blood cells. Every four days new colon cells and every three days new sperm. A popular statement you may have heard is that every 7-10 years every cell in our body has been replaced.

When it comes to your neural network your brain is in a constant state of flux. Every second your brain is making an unfathomable amount of shifts due to the ever-changing environment that you're in. As it's filtering all this sensory data, it's having to shoot off new signals to re-arrange and update itself. So even though it might not always seem like it, our identity is changing second by second, meaning that in life the only constant is change.

Very often when we're stuck in a rut and we can't move forward, (just like in the logical levels of change) it's because we fed ourselves a story about our identity being immovable, that life is a certain stuck way and we know our place in it. Let's picture identity as if it were your thermostat at home. What does a thermostat do? It maintains the temperature of the room within the set range you've set. The moment it goes below that level, the heating kicks in to bring it back, and turns the heating off if the temperature goes above the level. It brings your temperature back to the homeostatic point you've selected.

When we look at who we are, we can say metaphorically, just as an example, that I'm a 71 degrees Fahrenheit type person in temperature. My identity on the thermometer is a representation for the standards I hold myself to in life. I'm a 71 degrees person when it comes to my body, I'm a 71 degrees person when it comes to my finances, that's just who I am. I'm most comfortable at 71 degrees. If someone comes along and tells me I'm a 41 degrees person I just won't accept it. Same goes that if they tell me I'm a 91 degrees type person.

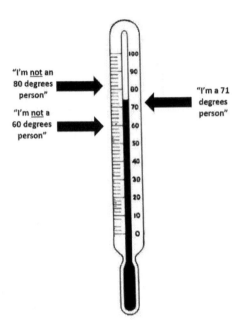

Let's go back to the limbic system (also known as the emotional mind, the chimp, or the inner child). Remember how its primary job in the brain is survival. It keeps you safe. It loves safety and my gosh it loves comfort. Imagine it as the health and safety officer in a company. It can't make the boss do anything it doesn't want to do, but it can add influence to sway the direction of the company.

Let's use our weight as an example. Many people experience dramatic fluctuations in weight, whether it's during holidays, Christmas or after a bad break-up. Let's say we start to put on weight. We could hypothetically say that the temperature on the identity thermostat went from 71 to 70 degrees. The belt's a little bit tighter, we might have to put it on a looser notch after a big meal. But we're not too worried about it because it's just a bit Christmas weight. Eventually the thermostat goes even lower, so we're now a 68 degrees person permanently on the looser notch on the belt. But again, we know we're well within range of getting back to where we were and being a 71 degrees person again. But before we know it, the temperature has dropped to 65 degrees and suddenly our identity thermostat kicks in, and says "Hang on a second, I'm a 71 degrees person, not a 65 degrees person". In that moment we take massive action to ramp up the heat to get us back to our 71 degrees standard.

Sound familiar? The same thing can happen when we are doing well in life. Sometimes when we've surpassed our standard we can sabotage ourselves. Let's say we hypothetically lost the Christmas weight, but kept going to the gym and kept eating well. Before we know it we've lost enough weight that we're on the tightest notch on our belt. Sometimes in that moment our identity thermostat can switch off the heat. We say "Hang on a second, I'm not an 80 degrees person, I'm a 71 degrees person", and we move back into our comfort zone. We stop going to the gym and we treat ourselves to foods we wouldn't have before. Often this is a very subconscious process and our identity thermostat can do this across the board – from our weight, to our positive habits, to our finances and much more.

So, here's a question for you. When did you decide that you were a 71 degrees person? Was it even you who made that decision? When I was younger I was always a worrier. I worried about when my homework needed to be handed in, I worried about what my friends thought of me, I worried about being picked last on Sports Day. My mum always said "Les, it's ok, you're just a worrier, you've always been a worrier". Now really she was trying to help, but what happened in that moment? My identity was created. I was a worrier. For years every Sunday night, without me realising what it was until I look back now in retrospect, I was suffering from anxiety because I'd be scared to go into school the next day. I accepted that behaviour as part of who I was. Why? Because I'm a worrier. But that changed!

Sometimes when a Doctor diagnoses us with depression or anxiety it can be extremely dangerous, because we get given a label. In Psychology they refer to this as 'sticky labels'. Once we are branded with that label it can often be difficult to remove. First of all, I'm in no way criticising doctors for diagnosing mental health disorders. I have spoken to some people who, after having a diagnosis, gave them an answer they'd been looking for and it made them feel so much better. But with mental health disorders it can really be such a grey area. Take a client of mine for example. Stuart was diagnosed with depression and no matter what we did it was difficult to make long-lasting progress because no matter how great he was feeling, a 9 out of 10 most days, there was a deep-rooted belief that it would come crashing down because he was depressed/a depressive person. I simply asked him a few questions as to how he was diagnosed. I didn't challenge him and I certainly didn't try to diagnose him myself, but it led to a really interesting conversation. He told me how he sat down with a doctor who asked him questions about his wellbeing for 20 minutes. After listening to him he diagnosed him with depression and put him on medication.

In the USA there's a great brain disorder specialist called Dr Daniel Amen. He's a psychiatrist who's done a few TED talks and has a great book called *Change Your Brain, Change Your Life*. In his book and during his talks he makes some really interesting points. This man has seen more brain scans than almost anyone else on the planet (over 100,000) so I value his opinion highly. He makes the great analogy that if we went to see the doctor about chest pains, we'd be quite worried if the doctor suddenly gave us medication. Quite rightfully the doctor would want to check for further symptoms and in most cases run some tests, whether that's an ECG or an X-Ray. The same as if you went in with bladder problems, before diagnosing anything they'd want to run urine tests. So why is it that when we come in with depression, anxiety or stress, the organ responsible for these symptoms isn't being tested? How can we diagnose someone as having heart problems if we don't test their heart? How can we diagnose a mental health problem when we're not checking the brain?

When I first brought this up with Stuart, as you can imagine he became very defensive at first. Why? Because like I said before, if we question someone's identity (suggesting they're a 44 rather than a 64 degrees person) our thermostat will not allow it. Once his guard came down later that week when he was at home, for the first time since his diagnosis, he began to wonder if maybe he was wired for happiness like everyone else. This lifted the wall in front of him and his progress excelled. But again, I'm not trying to dispute a label, I'm not trying to tell anyone they're something that they're not. All I'm saying is if we have an identity that is not empowering us then it is worth testing it.

Take a moment now to ask yourself those questions. When did you decide you were an X degrees person? Who made that decision for you?

Ok, great. We've been doing something really uncomfortable here which is questioning our identity. If we are not our biology, if our brain is in a constant state of flux, if our perceptions of events can always change, what makes me *me*, and you *you*?

71

The English psychiatrist Steve Peters answered this brilliantly in his best seller *The Chimp Paradox*, in which he talks about the relationship between the Chimp (the limbic system) and the human (the frontal lobe we recognise as us). In it, he suggests that we write down all the qualities that we wish to be and have as a person. So, that's what we're going to do now.

Give this a go now, I'm sure you can pull out at least 6 – 10 qualities.

Ok, so what did you get? What I love about this exercise is that there is likely to be a few similarities in a large group of people, but very often our lists are going to be completely different, and that's the beauty of it. According to Steve Peters, that list there is exactly who you are. The issue that we have is that the Chimp (our limbic system) often stops us from allowing those qualities in us to flourish. You may think there's an enormous gap between who you are right now and the person who is described in that list. However, out of the unfathomable amount of words you could have written in that list you consciously chose those qualities and that conscious decision was unique to you. If you want to be that person, you can be. What we are doing through this chapter is we're learning not just how the brain works but how to put certain methods into practice so that we can allow the real us to be brought to the surface and tame the Chimp.

Beliefs

Beliefs are not true. How many times have we believed in something only to find out we were completely wrong? Little spoiler alert here: When I grew up I believed in Father Christmas. Up until about 10, that man, that myth, that magic was real to me. Believing in that, despite it not being true, completely changed my emotional state. It made me feel ecstatic, excited, nervous, connected. Despite what I was believing not being true, those feelings were very real to me. Let's go back to when I spoke in How The Brain Works about the limbic system. It can't tell the difference between fiction and reality but that doesn't mean the emotional by-product of a belief isn't real. If you studied psychology at any point, you might be familiar with the term Placebo.

The term placebo effect is generally used in a medical arena. This is where people are given something and are told it is a real medical treatment, but it's not. This could be in the form of a pill, injection, even in a talking therapy. What's amazing however is that despite there being no medicine or no scientifically proven method given in the false treatment, patients can occasionally get identical results to those who have experienced the real treatment. This works across the board for all illnesses, including cancer, knee injuries, headaches, depression, vomiting and much more. In fact it's so powerful it will generally work between 18 – 80% of the time. Simply by believing that a sugar pill can cure my headache, approximately a third of the time it will!

What's really powerful is how effective the placebo effect is. In a great book called *Bad Science* by Ben Goldacre he recalls a time when Dr Stuart Wolf took two women who were suffering from nausea and vomiting and told them he had a treatment that would improve their symptoms. Just to make the whole procedure more believable, he put a tube down into their stomachs so they wouldn't taste the disgusting bitterness and gave them something called IPECAC. IPECAC is a drug which actually causes people to vomit and feel nauseous. So technically IPECAC should make the women's condition worse. Yet by manipulating their expectations and their beliefs, their gastric conditions were reduced. They got better! Their belief about something which was not true was far more powerful than the pharmacological influence.

Isn't that incredible?! That by changing our thought patterns we're able to alter our biochemistry to create the cocktail of chemicals needed to make us better.

So, what is a belief? We know now that beliefs are not real but it's beliefs that shape our reality. What we're really saying when we believe in something is that we feel certain about that. When we say "I believe in...", what we're saying is "I get a sense of certainty about...". Now that is a peculiar idea to get your head around isn't it? Beliefs feel very real to us, but because they're not concrete concepts it gives us extreme flexibility when choosing what beliefs we wish to have in our arsenal. To quote Tim Ferris "In a sense, our reality is negotiable".

All of us have particular beliefs that empower us. But we also have beliefs that limit us. We know from the logical levels of change that if we alter a belief, if we can take the handbrake off of the sports car we're driving, it's going to propel us forward even faster.

I want you to write down 3 limiting beliefs in your life that have produced unwanted or negative outcomes. After you've got those 3 I want you to write down what negative outcomes you've already experienced as a result of these beliefs. For example, years ago when I was 20+ stone (300+ lbs), one of my limiting beliefs is that I would never be thin and that I don't have what it takes to lose the weight. Now what negative consequences was I experiencing from that at the time? Well, I

74

would never take videos or photos of myself, I have very little evidence of me being that heavy. I had low confidence from that time, I never went swimming, and there was no way I was ever going to get a tan. It also stopped me going out with friends and enjoying life as it's meant to be enjoyed. These beliefs you have may be global beliefs. By global I mean beliefs about the way life works. These are normally beliefs which start 'Life is...' 'I am...' 'People are...'.

So really take some time to go into this, it's not always a pleasant exercise but it's necessary. This isn't about positive thinking, this is about seeing things as they really are. The first thing we need to do to stop driving with the handbrake on is to realise that we're doing it in the first place. Only when we can see in black and white what beliefs have been holding us back can we really start to alter them. Give yourself a good chunk of time to explore this, maybe even a whole evening.

What we'll find is that no matter what beliefs we have, they can be represented a bit like tables, they need legs to stand. We need to have reasons that can hold that belief up, because if we don't have any legs on our table (if we don't have reasons to believe that anymore), the table falls over, the belief topples. So how do we topple a limiting belief? We do it by replacing it with an empowering one. Remember, a limiting belief is not true! So, we might as well replace it with something that allows us to feel great and offer more value to other people. The empowering belief is often the opposite of the limiting belief you have noted down.

Let's run through an example. I had a client who came to see me a few years ago who was a nurse at the local hospital. A limiting belief that was holding her back both personally and in her relationship was that she wasn't attractive. Not only was this limiting belief affecting her but it was affecting her partner as well. You can imagine that the moment your beliefs become more powerful it can indirectly benefit the people around you too. By eliminating her limiting beliefs, the quality in her relationship soared. So, what did we do?

Her limiting belief was "I'm unattractive/ugly/unappealing/not sexy", so we created a new empowering belief in that session which was "I AM attractive/pretty/appealing/sexy". Can you guess what we're going to do now? That's right, we're going to start adding legs to this table. The more legs we have, the more the belief gets strengthened, the sturdier the table, and as a consequence the legs holding up our limiting belief will be taken away, and that table will fall.

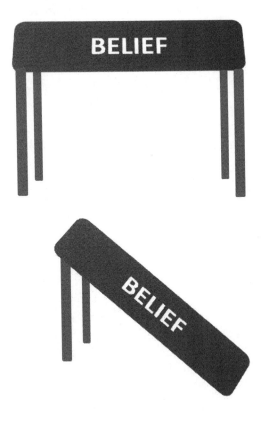

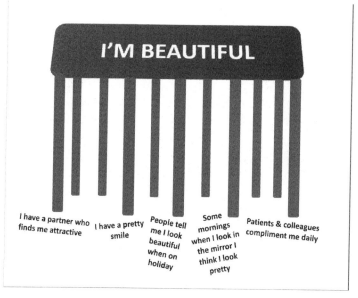

What are the legs of the table? The legs of the table are facts. They are real things, real reasons that prove that belief to be true to you. Just like in the Sparkling Moment we're going to have to exercise different parts of the brain that will find the reason why these things are true, and just like when we're building that muscle it's going to be hard. There is going to be times where we are convinced there's no more reasons, but just like the chapter on focus, we need to spend a little more time so we can fully shift the filters.

When I went through this belief exercise with the nurse, like all of us would, she really struggled at the beginning. In fact our session over-ran by an hour because I wanted to make sure we went through it properly. By the end (because she'd intensely exercised her brain and was seeing through the green filters) she eventually had a list of over 30 reasons why she was attractive! It started off small such as "I have a partner" and "I've been in a long-term relationship with someone and one reason they're with me is because they find me attractive". Then "One of my colleagues at work told me I have a beautiful smile", then she remembered other times patients had complimented her. Before long, even though it hadn't occurred to her at the beginning, she realised that she was frequently being complimented on her appearance and personality by colleagues, patients and eligible bachelors/gentlemen – and this would happen about 3 times a week. She started recalling memories she thought she'd forgotten: men wanting to talk to her in the park while she was writing poetry - interested in what she was writing, men & women complimenting her while she was on holiday, and then she even started to remember the times that she thought she looked good. Within a few hours we had it! A map of all the reasons why that belief is true. 30-40 legs re-enforced all in one place that made her feel empowered. This is a fantastic exercise for propelling you forward in the direction you want to go. These are big things we're talking about so it's important to give this the time it deserves. Keep pushing and searching for more. If it takes an hour, it takes an hour. If it takes 2 hours, that's ok! You can do this with all limiting beliefs!

Questions & Language

When we're thinking to ourselves, subjectively we're really running through a set of asking questions and answers. We know the neuroscience behind it but that's not how it feels is it. We're running through a series of words. It's amazing how much power there is in a word. Even when the intent is pure, something as simple as the wrong word can activate the emotional mind and send the amygdala into red mode. How many times have we had it in conversations when we've been annoyed by what someone said? If they had just phrased it a little differently they would have got the same point across but we'd be feeling fine. What would happen now if someone said "You're wrong", "You're mistaken" or "The reason it's your fault is..."? Just by starting a sentence with those words we can completely change the dynamic of a business meeting, or any conversation for that matter. Why? Because we've triggered the amygdala in ourselves or someone else.

Swearing is a perfect example of this. Whenever we're using taboo language we're using them for affect. We're using those words to tap into the emotional mind. If you've ever watched 'Talking Funny' (four of the world's best comedians come together to discuss how they write their acts), you'll see how much swearing plays a part in that. Jerry Seinfeld, Chris Rock, Ricky Gervais and Louis C.K are all in a room and of course the idea of swearing comes up. Three of the four swear heavily in their acts, but Jerry Seinfeld never liked to do it but recalls a time where he *had* to swear... and demonstrates that for the others. The bit is about his fury at the ineptitude of Superman's co-workers and how they cannot tell that just by wearing glasses Superman is Clark Kent! At one point he says "...even when every other week they're stuck in a fucking cave!". Now that there is such a simple sentence. He tried to do the bit many times but without saying the F word but found that he just wasn't getting the same laughs. The moment he added that word in, the laughs got better. In that context it expressed his anger for the situation better, which to the audience made it funny.

Even words that aren't taboo can cause a dramatic shift in any conversation. What about the word 'but'? When someone says a sentence to us and then adds the word 'but' in, it completely shifts the meaning to us doesn't it? I remember speaking to a spiritual healer once while doing my research into the benefits of spirituality. At one point I used the word 'but' and this healer jumped in and said "Everything before but is bullocks!". I've never forgotten that. The moment someone says "I like your shoes but…" it automatically erases the compliment doesn't it? We assume that the first part wasn't authentic and the real truth is coming up now. So, what can we use as a replacement for 'but' if we don't want our amygdala to raise its eyebrows halfway through that sentence? We can change the word 'but' to 'and'. If I said "I like your shoes but they'd look better in blue" you're not going to take in the compliment I've just given you, even if it was true. However if I said "I like your shoes and I think they'd look good in blue" the whole sentence has shifted hasn't it?

Just by language alone, even when describing our emotions, we can cause an emotional shift in our bodies. I remember once coaching a sales team and there was a great exercise I showed them about how powerful language is when it comes to our emotional state. I got one member of the sales team to stand up and tell me about the best holiday he'd ever had. As he told us about this music festival in Serbia we were hearing words like "fantastic" "awesome" "thrilling" "great", his body language was upright, his hands were moving everywhere and you could tell that just by recalling this he was feeling good. When I asked him how good the holiday was out of 10, he said 9. I then got him to recall the same memory but in it the only thing I wanted him to change was the language he was using. Instead of it being "fantastic", "awesome", "thrilling", "great" I wanted him to use neutral adjectives like "fine", "alright", okay". At first he started with the same body language – upright, hands going everywhere – but as he continued describing the holiday his head started lowering, his shoulders came forward and by the end his arms were crossed. When I asked him out of 10 how good he thought the holiday was, he said 7, maybe an 8 at a push. Isn't that crazy? The same experience, the same man, the same great memory, and just by changing the language he was using to describe it; everything else changed including his emotional state.

I want to talk about a few taboo words in this course, words that I refuse to hear at my seminars, retreats, classes or sessions. These are filler words, words which offer nothing other than uncertainty and a half-hearted approach:

Try

Why is there no reason to ever mention the word try? Remember the wise words of Yoda "Do or do not, there is no try". Why? Because try implies failure. The moment I'm telling you as story and I say "Steve tried to open the door" what do you imagine? That he couldn't, that there was some problem, maybe the door was stuck or locked? If I said "Steve opened the door" you don't imagine any of that resistance, do you? Same as if I asked you to "try to pick up an item next to you". Again, for a split second there would be a mild resistance because you'd be focused on why you might not be able to do it. If you ever go to a stage hypnosis show and the hypnotist has made someone believe their hands are locked together, the only word he'll ever use if he wants to strengthen that state is 'try'. "Go on Samantha, *try* and pull your hands apart. *Try* harder". But the more she tries, the more her hands are stuck together. The moment we try to accomplish a goal, the moment we try to lose weight, the moment we try to change the way we think, we've

81

already set ourselves up for failure. Using the word try is like giving the excuse before it's needed. There's no benefit to having it in our vocabulary. Let's replace try with 'will'. Instead of "I'll try that" say "I will do that".

Should

All of us should do something, but how many of us in the past took action on something we should do. "I should work harder", "I should lose weight", "I should go out more", "I should meditate". As Tony Robbins says "We should so much that we should all over ourselves". Again, should is such a limp word but if we change our should to musts suddenly our brain connects that idea with non-negotiable urgency. "I must work harder", "I must lose weight", "I must go out more", "I must meditate".

If

Remember what the Stoics said? There are only 2 things we have control over. Our thoughts and our actions. When we're dealing with the context of our thoughts and action, 'if' should be banished from our vocabulary. The reason for this is because we have control over our thoughts and emotions, the responsibility is on us to feel more confident and more congruent, we must change 'if' to 'when'. "If I stick to my new years resolutions", "If I lose the weight in time", "If I stop smoking" becomes "When I stick to my new year's resolutions", "When I lose the weight in time", "When I stop smoking". Simply by building the habit of using the word 'when', we send a signal to our subconscious mind that will reinforce those actions when its most needed.

There's an old quote by Confucius that says "Those who say they can and those who say they can't, are both usually right". And we can see why that's true now, can't we? Let's change our buts for ands, our shoulds for musts, and our ifs for whens, and let's stop trying and start doing.

At the beginning of the chapter I mentioned what thinking was. It's not just about the language we're using but the way we form that into questions and answers that can truly make an impact on the way we think. Coming up with a great solution to anything is very often linked to the quality of the question we ask. If we give ourselves a rubbish question, we're going to get a rubbish answer. If we're operating in a negative loop (within the emotional mind), and we ask ourselves a rubbish question like 'Why can't I lose any weight?' our brain will search for an answer. Because it is a bad question the kind of answer you're likely going to get is 'Because I'm a fat pig'. Let's say I didn't change my intent or the outcome I was looking for. What if I simply changed the question to 'How can I lose weight and enjoy the process every day?'. Suddenly I have to fire a completely different set of neurons to find a solution. Instead of saying 'I'm a fat pig', I might say 'I enjoy playing tennis a lot, I know that's good for me and it's not too much of a struggle' 'Actually there's some healthy dishes I really like the taste of so I can add more of those to my diet'. We suddenly have a solution, don't we? Not because I wasn't smart enough to think of it the first time, but because I asked myself the right question.

All the greatest innovations started with a thought, and that thought would have been based around an empowering question. 'What if this could be done better?'. One of my favourite questions I've ever heard is by Peter Teal, a major early investor in Facebook, "How can I achieve my 10-year plan in the next 6 months?". Simply by asking that question, we may find that it's not possible to achieve our 10-year plan in 6 months. It allows us to amplify our growth exponentially by finding what the road blocks really are. If we want to come up with better strategies in life then it's down to us to start asking better questions. If we want better results from others, then just by asking a better question we'll allow for their neurons to fire in a different way and this will produce a knock-on effect to the other neurotransmitters in their body.

Thinking and biochemistry is a bi-directional process. If we feel that we have gotten into a great habit but one day we're back to asking negative questions etc, it'll to be time to ask – 'am I biochemically sober?' If we're not releasing a healthy flow of neurotransmitters like serotonin then we'll very likely be thinking through the negative filters.

The Miracle Question

The Miracle Question is one of my favourite questions and I ask it to all my clients almost every session. It originally came from American psychotherapist Insoo Kim Burg. While helping one of her clients with depression she asked what it would take for this client's wellbeing to improve. The client replied 'It would take a miracle'.

Sometimes when we're in a really bad place, we believe that a miracle is the only way out of it. Thus, the Miracle Question was born.

Insoo Kim Burg then asked "Ok, so you're feeling a one out of ten. Let's say you go to bed tonight and have a wonderful sleep, and while you sleep a miracle takes place. Of course because you've been asleep you don't know a miracle's taken place. But when you wake up the following morning, you're no longer a one out of ten, you're a two out of ten. How would you know? What would allow you to know that that miracle had taken place?"

Wow, what a question! If we're coming from a negative place, if on a scale of one to ten we're starting at the very bottom, we're most likely to phrase the solution in a negative.

When clients have come to see me while suffering from depression or in a negative place at that time, when I ask this question the most common answer I hear is that "I wouldn't feel so bad".

Remember we need to focus on what we do want, rather than what we don't. The first step is therefore to flip it into a positive statement which gives us direction. If we don't want to feel XYZ, the next step I'd ask someone is "What **would** you be feeling?" or "What would be different?" if a miracle happened.

Once we've got a recognisable feeling/emotion, or definable concept to aim towards that's phrased in the positive; the next step is to find an action. If I was feeling tranquil, if I was feeling happier, if I had more energy... What would I be doing?

This is the next step within the Miracle Question... to have a definable action. For example, when I asked one of my clients the miracle question, they told me they'd be less stressed at work. I asked what they **would be** at work, to which they said 'more fun'. I then asked if they had more fun at work, what would they be doing? The client replied 'I would arrange group activities'. But remember, it has to be a definable action. They realised they hadn't had a work's night out for a few months so they decided they wanted to arrange one. Boom – we have a specific action. Now here's the most crucial step: What small step could they take between now and next week towards completing that action?

If you want to know the secret to goal completion it has been proven time and time again that it's in the small stuff where we find success... the baby steps. In an interview with actor Will Smith, when asked what his secret to success was he said "When I started, I didn't set-off to build a wall. My goal was to lay one brick each day, as perfectly as that brick could be laid. All I had to do was that one small action every day, and soon I had a wall".

When we're creating realistic goals for ourselves to achieve, the most sure-fire way to complete that goal is to break it down into its most achievable form and focus on that one baby step. Laying that one brick. Let's look at that question again. What SMALL step can you take towards the action? For the person who was stressed at work, the small step they suggested was to send a small group email out inviting their work-colleagues for drinks.

Once we have that small definable action, we have the last final segment of the miracle question, which is **when**. When can you put this action into place? And by when, we mean what day and what time on that day.

On a scale of 1-10, 1 being the lowest and 10 being everything you've ever wanted... where would you put yourself in terms of your happiness & wellbeing?

Circle below...

1   2   3   4   (5)   6   7   8   9   10

If a miracle took place which allowed you to be one higher on the scale, e.g. a 2 to a 3, what would allow you to know that the miracle had taken place?

Feeling
E.g. I would have more energy / I would feel happier

Anti-Feeling
E.g. I wouldn't feel so tired / I wouldn't feel so sad

_____
_____

I'd be less stressed at work

What **would** be different / how **would** you be feeling?

I'd be more fun at work

What would you be **doing** if this was the case?

I would be arranging a group event with my colleagues

What **small** step could you take between now and next week to do this?

I could send an email to my work colleagues asking if they'd be interested

What **day** and what **time** on that day will you do this?

Wednesday at 9.30am

On Wednesday at 9.30am I will send an email to my colleagues asking if they'd like to go for a drink next Friday after work

Give it a go yourself. Where are you/how do you feel on the scale of one to ten? One being the lowest you can imagine, ten being life on your terms. Once you've got that number, ask yourself the miracle question. If you woke up and a miracle had happened and you were one number higher, how would you know? Remember to frame it in the positive. What are you doing about it? Once you know what you're doing, what small step can you take in the next 7 days to work towards that action? And then finally, when?! What day and what time will you put this in place?

If you follow this simple map when it comes to breaking down your goals and making a strategy for a higher level of achievement and fulfilment - I can assure you that your results will go through the roof.

Tracking Our Thoughts

In 'our map of the world' I mentioned that we have 60,000 thoughts a day. 80% of them being identical thoughts to ones we had yesterday. Now for a lot of people, 60% of those can be negative. One of my favourite quotes is from Wayne Dyer: "I am what I think about all day long, and once you start realising that you start to become real careful with what you think about."

We've already spoken about what a thought is. Thoughts are billions of neurons firing in our brain. And we know from the questions and language chapter that thinking is usually just a series of questions and answers we pose to ourselves.

But who is 'ourselves'? What is the feeling of self we call 'I'? We know that it's not our emotions, we know that it's not our body. After all, if 'I' lost my leg I'd still be me – I wouldn't change. If 'I' felt angry one moment and happy the next, the feeling of being me doesn't change. The feeling of 'I' isn't even our memories. These physical and mental signals are all sensations that arise in consciousness.

No-one really knows what consciousness is. There are many theories, some of which state that it's a completely separate entity from our physical bodies, and some state that it's a by-product of our evolution. So far there is no proof that consciousness does exist outside of the brain but thankfully we don't even need to know what consciousness is for us to fully understand the benefits of it. If we refer to consciousness more like the internal awareness of our physical and mental; we can in effect track the thoughts that arise in our mind.

This is more popularly known as mindfulness. There's nothing mystical about mindfulness, it's simply a state of mind that's clear, non-judgemental and undistracted in its attention to the contents that arise to our awareness.

Mindfulness and meditation were first made popular over 2,500 years ago by the Buddha. Despite living in a Buddhist Centre to learn these teachings in more depth, I could not find a better description for the Buddhist explanation of meditation than in the book *Sapiens* by Yuval Noah Harari:

> "According to Buddhism, our feelings are no more than fleeting vibrations, changing every moment, like the ocean waves. If a few minutes ago I felt joyful and purposeful, now these feelings are gone, and I might well feel sad and dejected. So if I want to experience pleasant feelings, I have to constantly chase them, while driving away the unpleasant feelings. Even if I succeed, I immediately have to start all over again, without ever getting any lasting reward for my troubles.
>
> People are liberated from suffering not when they experience this or that fleeting pleasure, but rather when they understand the impermanent nature of all their feelings, and stop craving them. This is the aim of Buddhist meditation practices. In meditation, you are supposed to closely observe your mind and body, witness the ceaseless arising and passing of all your feelings, and realise how pointless it is to pursue them. When the pursuit stops, the mind becomes very relaxed, clear and satisfied. All kinds of feelings go on arising and passing – joy, anger, boredom, lust – but once you stop craving particular feelings, you can just accept them for what they are. You live in the present moment instead of fantasising about what might have been. The resulting serenity is so profound that those who spend their lives in the frenzied pursuit of pleasant feelings can hardly imagine it. It is like a man standing for decades on the seashore, embracing certain 'good' waves and trying to prevent them from disintegrating, while simultaneously pushing back 'bad' waves to prevent

them from getting near him. Day in, day out, the man stands on the beach, driving himself crazy with this fruitless exercise. Eventually, he sits down on the sand and just allows the waves to come and go as they please. How peaceful!"

What a terrific explanation – and an even better book which became a huge inspiration for this book! By building a habit that allows us to detach ourselves from the thoughts arising and being able to observe them through a mindfulness practise, it can allow us to diagnose when we're feeling stressed and more importantly stop it.

Many times I have found myself being hijacked by the emotional mind and like all of us, caught in a loop which could feel negative and only make us feel worse. Especially as we release cortisol into our body. By becoming conscious that my thoughts are negative and understanding that it's my fast paced, scared and negative inner dialogue that's causing me to feel bad; I can detach myself from that negative loop and allow those waves of thought to pass by like they did for the man standing for decades on the seashore.

By adopting a routine such as meditation or journaling we can strengthen the habit of being able to recognise when we're thinking negatively. This will allow us to either step out of the negative loop or tune our focus into the green filter so we can reduce the cortisol that has built up in our stress bucket, moving back towards becoming biochemically sober.

The Science Of Meditation

Mediation is a fascinating subject. Obviously by living in a Buddhist Centre for over a year and a half meditation has certainly become a big influence in my life. However, that's not what got me started in it. Meditation has been around for 2,500 years from the time of the Buddha but has expressed itself in many forms since then. Hypnosis is a form of meditation, as is daydreaming. If you drive I am sure you have experienced driving on the road for 20-25 minutes and suddenly thought 'Who has been driving?'... that's called Highway Hypnosis. We often do it when we watch television or when we're eating. All it is is a form of trance. The average person goes into trance every 7 minutes. If I asked you right now what you had for breakfast yesterday morning you may take a moment to recall it and while you do so, your eyes would go up and to the left or right. In that moment you're in a state of trance. All trance is is when the conscious and sub-conscious mind come together to focus on the same thing. When we're in that state we have access to make very powerful changes.

When I lived in the Buddhist Centre and was working as a hypnotherapist I remember speaking to a nun about hypnosis. Like many people I speak to she said "I don't like the idea of being hypnotised". I said to her "When you go to the Buddhist classes and one of the Kadams (Buddhist teachers) takes you through a guided mediation, do you enjoy that?". "Yes, I feel tranquil and serene, and I find it helps me" she replied. But the truth is hypnosis and guided meditation is the exact same thing. In effect you're daydreaming and someone is helping you to daydream about a particular concept.

When we're feeling a negative emotion we're generally in some form of trance. The limbic system can't tell the difference between fiction and reality. Negative trance is the perfect example of that. Let's use tomorrow as an example. If I wanted to, I could imagine tomorrow going really badly. I could imagine anything in the future going wrong. What am I doing when I'm imagining those things? I'm going into trance. I might see something in my head: it could be a still picture, a video, the sound of someone saying something negative to me. But either way I have to leave the present moment (the here and now) to go into trance to think about things. Just by thinking of those things, just by picturing those events going negatively tomorrow, the amygdala can send a message to the hypothalamus and release spikes of cortisol and adrenaline in my body. I'm altering my biochemistry through thoughts again. What happens next? I start to feel worried, and it feels so real to us. We could almost feel certain that it's going to happen. But the truth is tomorrow doesn't exist. Neither did the past. The only thing that truly exists is right here and right now.

The limbic system to some extent is always on alert. When we're walking down the street and taking each step it is constantly activated like a health and safety officer in our brain – always scanning the perimeter for danger. Why does the health and safety officer worry about the future? Because that's what a good health and safety officer does. By attempting to predict negative outcomes in the future, it's potentially avoiding danger which threatens our survival. By retrospecting negatively to the past it can update its information to see if it can aid us in the future. The problem we have as humans is we have that stress bucket don't we? Where all our negative thoughts become stored and accumulated through chronic levels of cortisol, the stress hormone.

Here's what meditation does. By drawing our attention to the present moment, by simply focusing on one thing that's happening now, the health and safety officer in our brain gets to calm down, our mind becomes less busy and the clarity of our situation increases.

In some way we can almost treat meditation like a cognitive re-boot, like the ultimate CTRL, ALT, DELETE to our mind. We can see on functional MRI scans that when someone has been meditating for just minutes, the blood flow in their brain has completely changed, and so does the electromagnetic field around their head. The thing that first swayed me into meditation was when I heard it was a regular habit performed by 80% of the world's top performers – from CEOs to sports athletes. I thought if it's good enough for them, it's good enough for me!

So, how do we meditate? You don't have to sit in some monastery or a cave somewhere, you can do it at home or anywhere quiet. I do suggest that when you start meditation you do so sitting up so that your mind is still alert; I personally find that if you try meditating lying down you will just go to sleep. You can literally meditate anywhere and at any time of day. I've meditated on planes and in the backs of cars, though my bedroom works just fine too. I personally find it is best to meditate shortly after exercise in the morning when I'm hormonally balanced and this sets me up for a great day.

What will we be doing in our meditations? Well frankly... whatever we want! There's thousands of different types of meditation available but in this particular section we're going to focus on clearing the mind. This is commonly referred to as Mindfulness Meditation.

Mindfulness is incredibly simple on paper but much more difficult in practice. I want you to find a comfortable position that you can sit upright in, perhaps on your floor, on your bed or in a chair. You can have your hands rested on your lap, from the tradition of Buddhism which I studied we would normally sit with the back of the right hand resting on the left palm with the thumbs touching, but if you want you can even sit with the classic Wisdom Seal if you prefer – touching the tips of the thumb and index finger together, forming a circle with palms facing up.

Before we start every session, we want to set clear expectations for what we want from each meditation. For this one it's of course a clear mind. Whenever we meditate we must have a focal point. What we're going to be doing in the video is focusing on the sensation of our breath entering and leaving our nostrils. We'll do this with our eyes closed. If you want at first you can do this listening to music, but it can be helpful to try it without sound. As we close our eyes we're going to pay attention to the sensations in our body, allowing us to feel more comfortable and release any tension we can feel anywhere.

As you sit there focusing on the sensation of every breath, different thoughts will likely appear. You might be sitting there for 5/6 seconds content and strongly focused, breathing in, breathing out, breathing in... and for dinner tonight I'll have... what happened in that TV show again? Certain thoughts will come up as distractions. The aim of this entire meditation is to simply recognise those thoughts, let them pass by and go back to focusing on your breathing. The best way to imagine it is that your mind is a clear blue sky and thoughts are like clouds just drifting through. We can certainly pay attention to them once the meditation is over, but in the moment we're not going to draw energy to it. We're not going to resist these thoughts coming up because even when we try to resist a thought we bring energy to it, don't we? The moment I want you to actively stop thinking of a black cat, you *have* to think about a black cat to then attempt to erase it. If you give yourself permission to think about it later and for now focus on your breath, you'll find it much easier to clear your mind.

Ideally you want to set aside 20 minutes for a meditation, especially at the beginning if it's a new habit you're trying to build. This may be challenging at first but as you continue to do this it will start to click for you.

Cultivating Gratitude

As I've already mentioned, we have a multitude of different emotions made available to us due to our biochemistry at any given moment. The emotions that we experience the most often are simply the emotions we've practiced the most. Practice through our actions, through our behaviours, our physiology, and our thought patterns. If you could experience only one emotion for the rest of your life what would it be? It can be different for different people. You may want to feel tranquil, serene, content, safe, excited or perhaps euphoric.

When it comes to our lifestyle as humans the number one emotion that will significantly boost anyone's wellbeing is gratitude. When we're feeling genuinely grateful it's impossible to be angry. Once we've cultivated gratitude, we no longer have expectations. As Tony Robbins said in the documentary *I'm not your Guru* "Trade your expectations for appreciation and your life will change in an instant". What a wonderful quote!

Due to our need to be constantly growing as humans it can be easy for gratitude to fall by the wayside. If we went back hundreds of years ago we'd be thrilled simply to have survived the Black Plague, yet now we've got billionaires who are looking to conquer death. Expectations have been great for human innovation but when it comes to measuring our happiness, historians often overlook a huge question – are we any happier? Our quality of life has dramatically improved when it comes to shelter, access to food, heat and the ability to communicate with the rest of the planet... but we already know that as great as these external comforts are, they're not related to us being biochemically sober. We know this by looking at studies of indigenous tribes where depression is reported as little as 1 in 2,000 people. Despite the western world being technologically and economically more advanced, *we* have the highest depression and anxiety rates on the planet, with some studies showing 1 in 3 people affected.

This shows us that expectations within the context of increasing our sense of day-to-day joy has no correlation. Before we strive forward to get what we want from life we must first learn to be grateful for what we already have. Like anything else, cultivating gratitude is a habit. As said in previous chapters, all it takes is enough deliberate practice for it to become second nature and a well-practised emotion. We just need to myelinate that neural pathway. In the next section I'm going to share with you an exercise that can help you start everyday with a spring in your step. When you're grateful nothing can touch you.

A Compelling Future

Even when you've learnt to become biochemically sober there's still going to be days where our resilience is tested. One day you'll be feeling on top of the world and nothing can stop you. It's in those moments when life will throw the curveball you weren't expecting. You'll have so many tools available to you from this course to help you find your way around that, but that doesn't mean it's an easy path. In moments of struggle one of the greatest things that can get us through is to have a compelling future.

A wonderful example of this is an experiment that was done at John Hopkins University. I personally find the experiment horrible, but it proves an incredible point. The experiment involved testing how long rats could tread water for before drowning. What would happen is the rats would be placed in what could only be described as a large bucket of water with the sides too deep for them to crawl out of which forced to tread water. What the experiment found is that rats would last an average of 13-14 minutes before giving up and starting to sink.

The experimenters then did another test. They took a new sample of rats, put them in a bucket of water, and around the 13 minute mark they'd take the rats out the water and allow them to rest. After the rat had retained its strength and its muscles were no longer fatigued, they would be placed back in the water. Can you guess how long they lasted in the water second time around? When I've given this question to people I find the answers range. Some people think the rats won't last that long, as they are surely fatigued despite resting. Others thought the rats lasted longer. What do you think? The truth is they lasted longer. But how much longer do you think they lasted? The optimistic people I speak to think they lasted 20 minutes, I've even heard some people even believe it could be

30. Believe it or not they lasted 60 hours! Can you believe that the second time they lasted 240x longer?! Why? This group of rats believed they were going to get saved. They'd had the experience of making it through before and this spurred them on to do it again, no matter what. Scientists do not necessarily believe it was hope which made them last longer but that belief gave them the energy needed to carry on.

This is just another great point that proves the logical levels pyramid which we discovered earlier in this section. The behaviour and results we are looking for can either be explored or capped at the level of our belief. If we went back to look at our ancestors in those hunter gatherer communities, their outlook for the future had to be positive to get them through the struggles of the day. If we didn't gather or successfully hunt any food today then we better believe we can do it tomorrow, otherwise the will to go on becomes negligible. It's important to note that we are the descendants of the genes that belong to the hunter gatherers that were able to create compelling outlooks for tomorrow in order to survive. An interesting thing to note here is that when anthropologists have spent time with indigenous tribes that live in nomadic hunter gatherer societies, they find that the tribe as a whole are a lot more focused about the imminent future than in many months or years. That makes sense when you think about it. Hunter gatherers had to live their life day by day. They didn't have fridges or freezers to store their food. Their shelters weren't as structurally sound as ours but they could survive and withstand extreme weather. The plants eaten would vary dependant on the season and they'd have to follow their prey depending on animal migration patterns. Remember they had very little belongings because this would just weigh them down when they were relocating. Their possessions had to only be what was essential to the tribe.

In modern society we spend huge amounts of time not just worrying about the imminent future like tomorrow, but in three months, sometimes three years time. The idea of worrying months ahead didn't really start until the agricultural revolution. The moment we started growing wheat it became a great calorie source for more people. Spending so much time harvesting this crop meant we went from hunter gather tribes to settled communities. As one of my favourite authors, Yuval Noah Harari, said "We didn't domesticate wheat, wheat domesticated us". What it also did was put huge pressure on our food source. By having a high calorie food source this led to a rapidly expanding population which then led to the vicious circle of having to plant more wheat. Now instead of worrying about our food source tomorrow for a group of 150 hunter gatherers we were worried about a harvest 3 months from now for over 1,000 villagers.

A perfect example in the disparity of mindset between the settlers worried about something in 3 months compared to a hunter gatherer nomad is when an anthropologist asked an indigenous hunter gatherer tribe "What will you be eating tomorrow?". The chief smiled and simply replied "Whatever we hunt and gather".

Like I have mentioned before, as much as it feels like we are, as much as thoughts about a fictional concept can give us the same feeling as if it were real, we are not clairvoyant. As we go into trance once every 7 minutes of course we're going to find ourselves daydreaming. Daydreaming about the future in a negative way very rarely helps us. I'm not suggesting you to stop daydreaming but I am saying if we are going to daydream about the future then let's make it a compelling one.

Worrying about the worst case scenario is like going to the cinema and watching the worst film you've ever seen and the moment its finished asking the projectionist to play it again. If that really happened you would walk out, wouldn't you? But remember *we* are the projectionist. This means as we daydream, as we go into that cinema, we might as well put on a film we like. That's what excitement is, isn't it? We get excited, we feel great right now when we have something to look forward to and when we have a compelling future.

I'm going to share with you a great technique that I found within Neuro-Linguistic Programming (NLP) so that in the moments we are worrying about the future, we can use this to instantly rewire our brain to make the future more compelling.

Swish Technique

Welcome to the Swish technique. This was made famous in the 1980s and is still used today. Why? Because it works! When we are feeling worried about something and imagining something going wrong, or even if we find ourselves stuck in a habit we want to change, this is a great technique to rewire the brain we're processing that information.

The way I want you to start this is by imagining the scenario you don't want. The one which has probably been running through your head already. Either way this is the unwanted outcome/action we're looking for. Take a moment to have that in your head and make it as vivid as you can. What I also want you to do is start to imagine the outcome you want. I want you to see it clearly. Is it like a photo or more like a movie playing? Is there any sound? If there is I want you to hear what you'd be hearing in that moment. Now pay attention to how you're feeling. How do you feel in your body in that moment? What happens to your breathing when everything is just the way you want it to be? Once you've made that image really vivid in your mind we can move onto the next step.

What we are now going to do is imagine the first image, the one we don't want, as if it were on a screen in front of us. Just in the bottom right corner of the screen we're going to have a miniaturised still of the outcome we do want. Once we've got that image clearly we're going to swap them over dramatically. I want you to make it as bright as you can and as quick as you can.

Let's start with the first image. It might be dull, boring, black and white... we're going to swap it over in 3, 2, 1... SWISH. The images have swapped over. The first image has faded into the background so it is in the corner, and all you can see now is the new image big, bright and full of colour. Everything just the way you want it to be. Now just hold it there, vividly in your mind, allowing that feeling to fill your body for 5 more seconds.

Ok, let's do it again. Get up the old image. Dull, boring, black and white.

We're going to swish over the new imagine in 3, 2, 1… SWISH.

The new image comes into view, even more powerfully this time. Feeling as if it could knock your head back. Full, bright, full of colour, everything just how you want it to be. …And just hold it for 5 more seconds.

I want you to do this task 5 more times in your head. Each time making that swish more powerful, making the new image bigger, brighter and better than before. Take as long as you need.

Now that we've done this, we're going to do something slightly different. I want you to now imagine the old image hanging in front of you, as if it was just a delicate pane of glass. The new image is behind it being slowly cranking away from you as if it were on a catapult. Just as the tension becomes too much, the new image catapults towards you, smashing through the pane of glass, sending shards of the old image across the universe. The new image now stands in front of you, fuller, brighter and more colourful than ever before.

Let's get that old image back up. Now at this point you might be thinking 'I don't want to put that old image up again'. Good, that's the point!

But let's do it again anyway. Place the new image behind the old image, and crank it back with the catapult. 3, 2, 1…. SWISH! And there it goes, smashing the old image once again, sending shards of glass everywhere and leaving the new image brighter, fuller and better than ever before.

Again, I want you to do this 5 times in your mind, at a pace that's best for you. Each time the power of that catapult becoming stronger, so you can almost imagine your head being knocked back as the new image is displayed in front of you.

Cleaning Out The Past

We have focused on the power of being in the present and we now know the importance of setting up a compelling future. It's important now to talk about clearing out the past. If something bad has happened to us in the past our mind cannot be at peace with it until we've figured out how it can help us in the future. That's the reason for memory. The only reason we remember the past is to survive the future.

Thankfully this doesn't involve years of counselling. As I was learning and qualifying in many different therapies, counselling was an option I was looking to explore at one point. I was soon steered away from that when I could see that other therapies, other tools and techniques were available that could not only get the same results as several years of counselling in a quicker time period, but often they could give better and more painless results too.

As much as the stereotype stays with us we don't need to go into the earliest realms of your childhood to fix you. Firstly, because you are not broken. Secondly, focusing on the problem won't give us a solution. The best thing about the past is that it's already happened and the past does not equal the future – unless you're living there. So, what tense are you living in? Where are you spending most of your time? Are you focusing on what you can control or what you can't control? Everything that's going right or going wrong? Are you focusing on everything that has happened, is happening, or might happen? Just from those three questions we can generally determine the quality of someone's life. If we're spending a lot of our time in the past it can act as another handbrake on the car while we're driving.

We all have attachment issues. There's always going to be something imperfect in our upbringing. But why is that? As mammals we generally spend a longer time being raised by our parents than other animal groups. But even among mammals, humans spend a far longer time developing than others. A baby zebra once its born can be running around in 6 hours. Even in primate groups, a chimpanzee will only spend 5 years learning how to survive. This is because the template's in its brain are a lot more developed than ours. Which in some ways is great because having more developed templates increases the chances of survival as they can fend for themselves quicker. However, our templates are nowhere close to being formed. There are certain algorithms which are coded within our DNA from birth. If you put anything towards a new born baby's mouth it will turn towards it and start sucking. The prime purpose of this is of course is so it can start sucking on its mother's nipple for milk. What would happen if the mother died during birth? What would happen if for some reason or another the mother could no longer feed that baby? Thankfully the algorithm is loose enough so it doesn't just require its mother's nipple. It is flexible enough that it can suck on any woman's nipple and therefore increasing its chances of survival. What we lack in our ability to be self-reliant at birth, we make up for in the long run through our adaptability. We can see that in a geographical sense, in the most dangerous corners of the planet, humans have found a way to adapt and live there. This is unlike any other mammal.

You can see from the many years involved in childhood that we are wired to be reliant on others, so we're always craving the love from someone. Whether that's our parents, siblings, friends or partners. We're not inherently screwed up as having that need is what got us here in the first place.

Understanding this is a great step to being able to clear out the past. We no longer have to do it under the guise that we have attachment issues. We can tell how well we have managed with the past by the way we remember the important events. If you recall memories that make you feel hurt, shameful or angry that are more than 18 months old it means your mind hasn't made peace and you're still carrying the weight of the past. By not resolving these issues your mind and body can continue to act in the present environment as if you're in permanent danger.

In 'How the brain works' I spoke about negatively retrospecting about the past and how we release those negative spikes of cortisol to a chronic level. By clearing out the past we can help empty any bits of stress at the bottom of that bucket. One of the ways we can do this is by journaling. But why use writing over thinking? In a peculiar way, writing is just a sophisticated form of thinking. By thinking things through normally it can allow us to reassess situations, perceive them properly and act intelligently. If we don't use the left-frontal cortex to think the difficult things through then we're more likely to make mistakes and potentially do damage to ourselves and others in the future.

Because thinking in our head involves 60,000 thoughts a day, writing them down allows us to see our thoughts as they are without any of the noise in our head. Simply by writing a difficult thing down we're able to start seeing it as it truly is, as opposed to worse than it is. One of my favourite tasks Tim Ferris talks about in his book *The 4 Hour Work Week* is addressing the worst-case scenario of something simply by writing it down on paper. The moment you start writing all those scary thoughts and situations (as bad as you can make them), 9/10 times when you read them back you realise they are nowhere near as bad as you first thought. I really urge for you to give this a go because it's amazing to feel the difference once it's out of your head and on the paper. One of the loveliest things about journaling is when you write about the personal important matters throughout the course of a week or month, or even just the bad memories that keep coming up, you'll very likely start to notice a pattern within them and therefore start to identify the causes of events and actions that might hurt you.

Many times in the past I've tried to start a journal and fail miserably. Not only because I 'tried' but because it was something I felt I *had* to do every day. This isn't something you *have* to do every day. If you don't want to do it at all that's fine. But it's when I started to understand the science behind why journaling works that I started doing it properly and got hooked. There are days now where I feel I can write an essay.

If there's something that's more than 18 months old which still gives us negative feelings when we think about it, it means we haven't fully learnt from the experience yet. I'm going to take you through a series of powerful exercises that once addressing those uncomfortable memories will actually move the location of it from the emotional mind into the intellectual mind, making it a memory which you have control over. By going through these memories one by one it will be like taking out the trash, allowing the handbrake to come down on that car so we can start driving at full speed.

Achievement Vs Fulfilment

I want to break a couple of myths that I feel we've all been heavily mis-sold in the western world. Something we often hear in the personal development world is to 'Complete your goals', 'If you want to be successful, you have to have goals!', 'If you want to be happy you need to be successful and be goal orientated', 'You need to be a high achiever'. But… when it comes to fulfilment and that feeling of contentment, experiencing the general sense of tranquillity and serenity available to us in every moment that we search our lives for; setting goals couldn't get us further away from that. To understand that we have to recognise that there is a difference between achieving and fulfilment.

A classic blueprint to success and living a good and happy life that most of us have been sold can generally be covered under the following: To increase your happiness you need to get good grades at school. Why? So you can go to a good college. What happens when you're at college? You need to get good grades so you can get a good job. After a good job you need to get that promotion. You need to have a stable relationship, potentially a couple of children, and when you've done that you can finally be happy. You have successfully followed that western blueprint and lived the nuclear family. Now I'm not arguing that people who live in that dynamic can't be happy. I'm sure there are many people living that lifestyle who feel extremely fulfilled day to day. But we would have to be insane to believe that's the only way it can be done. What happens to most of us when we get to that place, is that the feeling we've been waiting for doesn't arrive. We start to question everything and something that's unique in these cases is we have a midlife crisis. Can you imagine the sheer confusion that from the beginning of your life to that point thinking you were going to get the pot of gold at the end of the rainbow, only to find it's not there? It's quite well known that when the astronauts came back from landing on the moon they started suffering from depression. Why? Because after you've gone to the moon, what on Earth else are you going to do with your time? (pun intended!) What's next...? You've achieved your ultimate goal. Based off the western blueprint, surely achieving your ultimate goal would leave you feeling happy for the rest of your life? But we know that's not the case.

When we write a list of goals what is it that we're looking for? When we write down on our bucket list that we want to skydive, travel the world, swim with dolphins, have a family... what are we really looking for? We're looking for the feeling it's going to give us and we're looking for an excuse to get back to the present moment. But as we already know it's us that gives us that feeling and that the only thing that is real is now. We know that goals won't get us there.

If you've read any of my blogs or watched my online videos you will know that I can't stand fridge magnet philosophy. What do I mean by that? The cheesy quotes which everyone knows but nobody puts into practice. But if there's one thing those darn fridge magnets got right, it's that happiness and fulfilment is not a destination but a journey. There's never an excuse to wait to be happy. By the end of this book you're going to have learned how to master your biochemistry. Your body is going to flourish like never before and your thoughts are going to feel clearer and more positive than you've ever been used to. But If you're waiting to be happy you're never going to open the gift that is you, right here, in this present moment.

What is achievement? What is the point of doing anything if everything we could possibly want feeling wise is available to us now? Because achieving makes our lives richer.

Earlier on when I spoke about tracking your thoughts and the science behind meditation we became aware of the present moment and it allowed us to focus on different sensations such as the feeling of sitting down, pressures which may have been on our shoulders, tensions and vibrations in our body. I talked about consciously tracking the thoughts which arose and allowed them to pass by us like a cloud passing in the blue sky. It allowed us to become aware of the awareness we recognise as us. By simply working on recognising that our awareness and our thoughts and feelings are separate, by being conscious of the sensations which arise - our baseline of fulfilment increases. Those negative sensations that we experience when feeling bad simply become sensations that are presented to us which we can consciously let go.

No-one really knows what consciousness really is. As mentioned previously, some people believe it's just a by-product of the brain firing, some believe it's something which exists separate from the body and some believe in a soul. Whatever you believe about consciousness doesn't matter because it doesn't change the fact that being a conscious being allows us to enjoy the sensations that are available to us as humans. We can simply enjoy what it's like to live wealthily. We can enjoy the feeling of making love, contributing and giving value to others, the adrenaline rush of a sky-dive. We can even start to enjoy the negative sensations that arise in the past because it's all part of this wonderful tapestry that is life. What this also means is that by taking control of the present moment and remembering we are our biochemistry, we no longer become subjected to needing and craving things outside of ourselves.

I remember on my 26th birthday when I was living at the Buddhist Centre, getting the call from one of the nuns to inform me that throughout the day while I'd been out my room, I had been burgled. Someone had broken in and taken the majority of my possessions. I was told I needed to come back quickly to provide a statement for the police. Now at first I thought she was joking – I thought 'I know what these sneaky Buddhists have done... they're throwing me a surprise birthday party' and

I looked forward to coming back to enjoy some cake with friends. I went back home as instructed, went through the front door where I was greeted by the nun and joked "Alright, where's the stripper that you've hired?!", as to which she laughed and replied "He's in there, dressed as a Policeman". But much to my dismay the Policeman wouldn't take his clothes off…. no matter how hard I insisted! I spent the next half an hour looking around my room which had turned into a crime scene, making a list of all the objects which had been taken. The burglar had taken my laptop, my camera, my clothes. For some reason he even took my bedroom lamp… anything he could get his hands on.

What I loved about that moment is that I realised I had hit a new milestone when it came to my emotional development. I wasn't upset, angry or scared that my possessions had been taken. I had fully grasped the ideas which I've taught here in this chapter, which is that my happiness is not attached to something external to me. Afterwards my partner took me out for a lovely meal and I enjoyed the rest of my birthday. Going back to the stoic philosophy… the burglary had already happened and it was out of my control, so why worry? When you adopt the philosophy of enjoying everything and needing nothing, that's when your life changes in an instant and your problems cease to exist.

Achieving allows us to grow and explore new sensations that life has available. We have a finite amount of time and as far as we know we have just one life time. That's why we want to achieve… because we can. There is nothing more exciting than exploring the infinite potential inside ourselves. Whenever we feel that we've gone all out and given 100% we always find out there's another level. There's always more we can give. Our physical body can always improve and our capability for emotional growth is infinite. You can always be richer and you can always be more generous.

You can see why achievement and fulfilment are not the same thing but they go hand in hand. Instead of looking at achievement as the destination that holds permanent fulfilment, we can recognise achievement as the road and fulfilment as the vehicle we drive.

THINK Chapter Summary

- The way that we think determines the way that we feel (our biochemical reactions). The way that we feel determines we way that we think. It's a bi-directional process.

- We have 2 million year old software (limbic system) in our brain that is responsible for negative, obsessive, vigilant and non-innovative thoughts, and it cannot tell the difference between fiction and reality. The reason for the limbic system is seeing things negatively and obsessively etc helped us to survive as cavemen. Although we are no longer exposed to the imminent dangers we once did, we still have the ability to panic, feel fear and experience increased stress to things that do not threaten our survival. This can be a gradual process and is often caused by negative thinking.

- All of our negative thoughts are stored and accelerated in a 'stress bucket'. This stress bucket is actually a build-up of stress hormones (such as cortisol). Cortisol is helpful for us in small doses but in chronic amounts it can be dangerous to our immune system and overall health e.g. increased aging.

- Our environment/reality is all happening inside our brain, due to the way our neurons are being fired and wired together.

- It's not events that cause happiness or stress, but our perceptions/meaning/stories we tell ourselves about those events that cause emotions (biochemical shifts). We have the ability to shape our reality by changing the meaning we give events that have happened in the past or present.

- Our brain is more like play-doh than it is porcelain. The qualities of our brain are very similar to muscle in that we can 'grow' certain areas by exercising them. This is called myelination. A part of the brain that is related to logic, positivity and regulating control is the left-frontal cortex. Through neuroplasticity we can exercise the left-frontal cortex.

- For our brain to change we must do something repeatedly. If we stop taking a particular action then the neural pathway involved with that action will begin to erode (if you don't use it, you lose it!)

- If we want to move towards a certain goal we need to focus on what we want rather than what we don't want. What we focus on or actively do not focus on is where our mind will guide us. E.g. Car crashes/colours.

- When we focus on anything with intent then other stimuli will move into our unconscious blind spot.

- We have the ability to focus consciously on approximately 7 things at a time. The rest are perceived subconsciously. The 7 things most important things at any given time are presented to our conscious mind by the subconscious through the reticular activating system.

- When we tune our reticular activating system into different criteria we'll suddenly start to notice different things. E.g. When you buy a new car you'll start seeing that car everywhere.

- By recalling positive moments that have happened in a previous time period we have the ability to exercise our pre-frontal cortex. The term 'exercise' means coming to a block and pushing through. This strengthens/myelinates the neural pathway.

- If we want an element of our life to change we have the ability to go deeper inside ourselves to make that change more effective and longer lasting. The levels of change are Environment, Behaviours, Capabilities, Beliefs, Identity and Mission/Spiritual Beliefs.
- Due to our brain being in constant flux our identity is ever changing. Our identity is linked to our standards in life and our standards are like a thermostat where we have the ability to change the gauges.
- Our identity is our left-frontal cortex. We may not always feel that we match the identity of our left-frontal cortex and this is because the limbic system is holding is back.
- If we have a disempowering identity of ourselves and our capabilities then it is vital we test our theories.
- Beliefs are not true. They are a state of certainty which we have the ability to strengthen or weaken. This can be done through the belief table exercise.
- Language and questions have the ability to activate different neural pathways and networks. By using different language with ourselves and others we can alter an outcome.
- Some language that is taboo can activate the emotional mind.
- By changing the questions we ask ourselves (to an empowering solution focused question) we can change the firing of our neural networks to give a more quality solution.
- When we refer to our sense of self, 'I', we're actually referring to the awareness of our actions, thoughts, feelings and sensations.

- By becoming aware of our thoughts and increasing our understanding that we are not our thoughts, we can recognise when we enter negative loops and regulate our emotions better. This is known as mindfulness.
- Mindfulness meditation can help reduce the activity within the emotional mind and can allow us to live more in the present moment.
- On top of being mindful one of the greatest emotions we can practice is gratitude.
- For us to get through difficult times in the present, as well as being mindful, having a compelling future can get us through tough times. Hope can increase energy and resilience.
- Clearing out the past involves removing our limiting beliefs and negative memories. If there is a memory from more than 18 months old that still creates a negative emotional response in us, it means we haven't learnt from that experience. If we haven't learnt from it we cannot move on.
- Memories give us an arsenal of templates to use so we can increase our chances of survival in the future. By journaling and going back through our uncomfortable memories to see what we could have done differently our mind learns from the event and no longer treats it like excess baggage.
- Achievement and fulfilment are not the same thing.
- We feel incredible when we achieve as continuous growth makes us happy. However, we also need to master our ability to be fulfilled. By learning to be fulfilled in everyday moments while we continue to move forward achieving we will experience an increased sense of wellness.

<u>BREATHE</u>

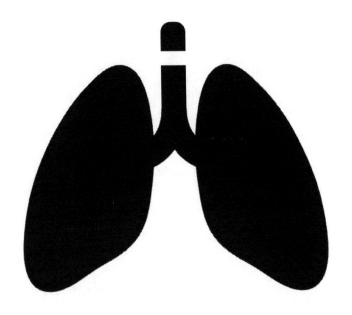

"Breath is the key to the door of our physiology"

Lester Savage

The Primary Connection

Life begins with our first breath. The inhalation of oxygen is by far the most essential ingredient to a healthy life. We can go for a week without sleep, a month without food, years without social connection, days without water, yet for some of us only a minute or two without breath.

Even the word spirit comes from the Latin word Spiritus which simply means breath. Yogis have been using their breath for thousands of years to enter altered states of consciousness. More and more scientific research is showing that by simply changing our breathing we can alter the rest of our physiology and biochemical reactions.

Breath is vital, it is the key to the door of our physiology. For us to understand this we need to know a bit about how the autonomic nervous system operates. The autonomic nervous system is a set of nerves in our body that connect to the heart, blood vessels, smooth mussels and glands. It's divided into two parts: the sympathetic nervous system and the parasympathetic nervous system. The sympathetic prepares the body for action by sending signals to the adrenal glands, which secrete the hormones I've mentioned previously such as cortisol, adrenaline and noradrenalin. When our sympathetic nervous system has been activated we'll experience things like dilated pupils, increased heart rate, sweaty palms and quick breaths our blood supply to the heart increases and our digestion system inhibits. It's simply the fight/flight response. The parasympathetic nervous system keeps the body calm and conserves vital resources, usually kicking in once the sympathetic nervous system decreases. The main indicators of this are regular or decreased breaths, constricted pupils, decreased heart rate, decreased adrenal gland activity, have full blood supply to our blood organs and our digestion system is stimulated.

In effect the sympathetic and parasympathetic nervous systems are opposites of each other. To make it easier for us to understand: when we're in the fight/flight anxious mode, the sympathetic nervous system is being used and this causes our breath to speed up. When we're feeling relaxed and calm as if there is no danger around, the parasympathetic nervous system kicks in and our breath slows down.

Remember, breath is the key to the door of our physiology. But what does this mean? It means that even though we know our breath changes depending on which nervous system is being activated. We can also consciously alter which system is being used by the way we change our breath. Just like thoughts and feelings, it is a completely bi-directional process and breath is the first step. In short, the quickest way to change how we feel is by the way we moderate our breath.

Very often when we're experiencing panic attacks we'll be using the sympathetic nervous system to create that. Our breaths get so much quicker that we forget to exhale properly.

Back in 2016 when I learnt to scuba dive I really struggled at the beginning to feel calm and manage my breaths underwater. Occasionally I'd find myself continuing to take large inhalations from the scuba tank and forgetting to exhale. What this meant was that even though I had enough breath in my body and enough oxygen circulating, I had tricked my mind into thinking I couldn't breathe properly. I was trying to pack another inhale on top of lungs which were already filled with oxygen, giving the illusion that I couldn't breathe! My instructor at the time was a tiny little French man called Paul. He told me, in his seductive French accent, "You need to focus on your exhales". By focusing on exhaling I would empty the air already in my lungs allowing me to then take a full breath in. This would allow me to start making a regular breathing pattern, moving my body from the sympathetic nervous system to the parasympathetic nervous system.

Remember, if you're having a panic attack, "fo-kess on yaw hex-ales!" (It's hard to write in a French accent...)

Breath Awareness & Conscious Breathing

Breath awareness is like Ronseal... it does exactly what it says on the tin! It's the ability to increase our awareness of the frequency and quality of our breaths. How many breaths are you taking in a minute? Are they long or short? Full or shallow? After all we cannot change what we are not aware of. I want you to try this little exercise. Time yourself just for 1 minute and count how many breaths you're taking in that minute and write down how many you took. How would you describe their quality? How do you feel in your body when you're feeling this way?

Ok, how many breaths did you take? Was it 6? 10? Over 20? For us to be in a calm and relaxed state using the parasympathetic system, as well as delivering the right amount of oxygen to our bodies and increasing the functionality of other bodily processes, we should be taking no more than 15 full breaths in a minute. In an ideal world, if we're feeling tranquil, it should be between 6 and 10 full breaths. However, if the number of breaths you took then, or throughout an average day is closer to 20 or more per minute, it means that even if you have been sitting at a desk all day there's a part of your body that believes you're being chased by a sabretooth tiger. You may have even been aware of how often you hold your breath. But something that we can start doing to diagnose if there's any tension in our bodies is occasionally throughout a day timing how many breaths we're taking in a minute.

Here's another exercise. Time yourself for a minute again, but this time I want you to aim for 6 full breaths. On average you want to be inhaling for 4 seconds and exhaling for 6 seconds. We always want to make sure our exhales are longer than our inhales (Remember what little tiny Paul said – focus on your exhales!). It doesn't really matter whether you're breathing through your nose or mouth, whatever is most comfortable for you. Personally, I breathe in through my nose and out through my mouth for this task. Again, take notes after you've done this for a minute to see what you notice. After you have taken 6 full breaths with longer exhales, how do you feel? What differences do you notice?

What we're doing here is breathing consciously, mindfully, intentionally. We're breathing with a purpose. It's also been referred to as coherent breathing. Breathing consciously in this way increases something called heart rate variability (HRV) which is the variation in the time interval between heart beats. Low HRV is commonly found in people that worry more as well as in those who suffer from Post-Traumatic Stress Disorder, but by increasing our HRV we can shift our brain and body from that stress response to the state where we regain control. Coherent breathing is the quickest fix I know to shutting off the stress response and activating the pre-frontal cortex.

When scientists have measured people at different breathing rates they've found that there are 'sweet spots' linked to each person - a resonant rate where the electrical rhythms of the brain, the heart and lungs become synchronised. On average this would equate to 3 and a half to 6 full breaths per minute. So, find the sweet spot which is best for you. Is it 4 seconds in and 6 seconds out, or perhaps 6 seconds in and 8 seconds out?

If you're worried at the amount of breaths you took in the first exercise do not be alarmed. In no point throughout this book do I want you to beat yourself up about where you currently are. This book is not about positive thinking, it is about intelligent thinking. As mentioned before, the first step to moving forward is recognising where we currently are. Not making it worse than before, just seeing it how it actually is. We can't build a road to where we want to be if we don't have an accurate starting point. One of my favourite quotes about recognising negative patterns is by Vernon Howard in his book *The Power of Your Supermind*:

> *"Encourage yourself by remembering that any detection of negativity within you is a positive act, not a negative one. Awareness of your weakness and confusion makes you strong because conscious awareness is the bright light that destroys the darkness of negativity. Honest self-observation dissolves pains and pressures that formerly did their dreadful work in the darkness of unawareness. This is so important that I urge you to memorize and reflect upon the following summary: Detection of inner negativity is not a negative act, but a courageously positive act that makes you a new person."*

Our State

Our state is a term used casually in many conversions, "he's not in a great state right now", "wow when she was standing on stage she was in such a powerful state". But when we're talking about state or mood, obviously our biochemistry has a part to play in this. But what do we really mean by state? We don't necessarily have to be biochemically sober to experience a good state. Our state is really made up of 3 things: Our internal representations (our map of the world), our behaviour/actions and our physiology. We've already gone into internal representations in quite some detail from looking at what we focus on to the language we're using, but we haven't quite gone into physiology in as much detail yet. We already know that breath is a perfect example that slots into physiology. The moment we change our breath, our state changes. We can go from a panicked state to a calm state simply by changing our breath. There are other elements in physiology that are worth mentioning: how you hold your body when you're walking or sitting can very often be the determining factor of the state you're in. In fact, just to show you how linked physiology and the way that we feel are, have a think about this scenario...

If I ask you to imagine walking through a door and on the other side there are 2 men. You can't talk to them nor can they to you but the knowledge you have been given beforehand about these people is that one is ecstatic as he'd won the lottery and is getting married tomorrow. The other is depressed and has just this moment filed for divorce as well as bankruptcy. Without them taking any actions, without being able to monitor their behaviour, without being able to ask them questions and hear the language they're using, I am sure it would be obvious to you which one is which simply by looking at their physiology.

Let's take the depressed guy first. Will he be standing up or sitting down? Will his shoulders be pinned back or slouching forward? Will his head be looking up or looking down? Will his breathing be deep or shallow? Will his face be smiling? How do you know this? Because you're human and we've all practiced this before. When we feel negative, upset or disempowered our entire physiology changes. Again, this is a bi-directional process. If we consciously change our physiology, so to can we change our emotions.

Here's another exercise I want you to do. Get into a position which feels natural for you and I want you to try to feel awful. Go to that bad place, allow your shoulders to slouch forward, put your head down and breathe the same way you do once you've given up. Are your legs and arms crossed? Are they simply limp and open by your sides? Feels horrible doesn't it?! Ok, don't worry though as we're going to change that.

Stand up if you've been sitting down, shake your body out, we're going to go again! If you want to do this in front of a full-length mirror that'd be great but if you don't have one available that's ok. Again, I want you to try your best to feel bad. Feel the same as you did before but this time you'll be standing up. I want you to pin your shoulders back, look up slightly (a 45 degree angle) and smile ear to ear. It doesn't matter if you feel silly, it's just a fun little exercise. Do it. Loosen up. Shoulders back, head up, smile ear to ear... close your eyes if you like. Now try to feel as bad as you did before. If you start to feel at all similar to how you did first time around then recheck your physiology. It means your shoulders will have started slumping forward and your smile will be less wide. I mean it – keep those shoulders pinned back, head up and smile like you're grinning ear to ear. I want you to be grinning like a fool... You can't feel as bad, can you? You cannot feel as bad unless you've changed your physiology to get there.

If we want to put ourselves in an empowering state the first thing we need to do is change our breath, closely followed by the way we're holding ourselves. By consciously altering our physiology the rest of our body follows.

The issue we have in modern day society is that we are indirectly being forced to place our posture in a disempowered depressed position. When you look around in an office and see people sat in front of a computer, very rarely are they sat with their backs straight and their shoulders pinned back. When we are sitting in the car the exact same thing can be said. We're forced to move closer to the foetal position and away from an empowered stance. When we're sitting on the sofa watching television a lot of us aren't even sitting. Instead we are lying down. This means that in a conscious day that's approximately 16 hours long, 12 hours of that (75%) we are forced into a disempowering physiology. You know how difficult it was to feel awful when maintaining a confident and empowering physiology. You can only imagine how difficult it is to feel empowered, even just feeling fairly positive, when we're spending 75% of our time with a disempowered body. There's a fantastic TED Talk by Roger Frampton that talks about a study looking at backpain. The researcher found that in indigenous tribes and in countries that suffered very little back pain, their lack of pain all seemed to link to a J shaped spine. A lot of us in the western world have an S shaped spine. But again, this isn't a genetic tendency. All of us are born with J shaped spines but if we're forcing ourselves into an unnatural position for 12 hours a day and for decades of our life, our body evolves to compensate for that habit. As a symptom of that over compensation we get back pain.

Here's a little test for you. Take your shoes off wherever you are and I want you to squat as low as you can without taking your heels off the ground. Now you should be able to do this effortlessly, but most of us in order to regain balance have to lift our heels off the floor so we're perched on our toes. A 3 year old will be able to do this without straining, in fact they should be able to sit in this position very comfortably because their spines are still in that J shape. You can see that something as regular as back pain is just another evolutionary mismatch.

Just like chimps and bonobos, our sitting position used to be the deep squat but seats screwed that up for us. The next time you find yourself in a disempowered state change your physiology and breathe and take notice of the way things have changed.

Mitochondria Part 1

Where does energy come from? We already know that the quality of our cells is responsible for the quality of our health, but where specifically does the source of that energy originate? The answer lies in an organelle (organ of a cell) called mitochondria. Mitochondria are like microscopic power stations, pumping out a chemical called ATP (Adenosine triphosphate). Just like I mentioned neural-pathways being the currency in our brain of how we process sensory information, ATP is the currency of energy, and there are 1 quadrillion (1,000,000,000,000,000) mitochondria in our bodies. We have on average 37 trillion cells in our body and every single one of those cells has thousands of mitochondria.

The primary food source for those mitochondria? You guessed it... oxygen! If we're spending the day hunched over and breathing shallow then our mitochondria are simply not getting enough oxygen to effectively produce the energy we need or desire.

One of the most elegant ways I've read mitochondria being described is by David Perlmutter in *Power Up Your Brain*. In one section he refers to mitochondria as 'the conductors of the genetic orchestra that regulate how every cell ages, divides and dies. They wave the batten which dictate which genes are switch on and off in every one of our cells.' Now as well as this, mitochondria provide the fuel for establishing new neural networks. 20% of the oxygen we're using is used by our brain. We know that if we're not breathing properly it's going to affect our athletic performance. It's the way we breath that dictates whether we're in an aerobic or anaerobic state. As our brains are oxygen swallowing machines, we forget that if we're not giving it the oxygen/fuel it needs it will also affect things like our memory, productivity and decision-making skills.

Going back to our breath awareness and physiology, are you breathing full or shallow? Do you look like Clark Kent or Superman when you're taking big breaths? Do you look like Wonder Woman as you're inhaling the fuel needed for our minds and bodies to work at their optimum?

Most of us have actually forgotten how to breathe properly. Many people, when you ask them to take a deep breath, will breathe fully into their chest/upper body. But this stops us from getting a full breath. To be able to breathe deeply we need to be breathing fully into our lower body. It should be as if we're inflating a balloon within our stomachs. You can see this perfectly in a new born baby lying down sleeping – as its taking breaths into its body you won't see its chest rise at all, merely it's stomach. Just by breathing with bad posture into our chest we can be affecting our ability to breathe by up to 30%. Think about that for a moment... can you imagine what giving 30% less fuel to your cells could be doing to them? If anything, it's like you're working day to day at high altitude without any of the benefits. Let's twist it round... can you imagine how much better you would feel if your cells were 30% more optimised?

So, let's change our posture. Sit tall or stand tall as if you've got a book on your head. Chest up, chin down. Breathe into your diaphragm. I want you looking like Superman or Wonder Woman. Breathe and hold yourself like the most powerful version of you. I want you breathing correctly. As Doctor Arthur C Guyrm said "All chronic pain, suffering and diseases are caused by a lack of oxygen at the cell level. We want to nourish the cells of our bodies with oxygen and optimise the function of our bodies on all levels".

Detox/Lymph System

What is the lymphatic system? Essentially the lymphatic or lymph system is a series of thin vessels carrying a colourless liquid called lymph. This lymph contains a high number of a type of white blood cell called lymphocytes. These are the cells that can help fight infection and eliminate damaged or abnormal cells. So how does it work?

1. Blood circulates around the body
2. Fluid leaks out from the blood vessels into the body tissue creating tissue fluid.
3. This tissue fluid collects all the waste products, bacteria and damaged cells.
4. This special liquid will drain into the lymph vessels
5. The lymph vessels filter this fluid through a lymph gland which removes any of the damaged or sick cells and unwanted waste products.
6. The remaining lymph, having removed the unwanted waste, slowly circulates through other lymph vessels before being emptied back into blood circulation.

In essence, our lymph system is our detox system and is responsible for 70% of the removal of our toxins! We know that sickness is caused from the build-up of toxins and that's why the lymph system is so important when it comes to eliminating them. It's so vital to our quality of life that if it were to stop working for 24 hours we would die.

We know that when it comes to our blood circulation our heart acts as the pump to transport our blood and nutrients effectively. But our lymph system doesn't have a pump. What causes our lymph system to work? Our breath! Our breath works as the pump, pushing the lymph through our vessels to effectively eliminate waste. Again, if we're not breathing deeply, if we're not breathing properly, we're as good as minimalising our capacity to detox! Instead of having the trash in our bodies taken out every week, it's like someone's taking the trash out every month. Quite obviously, that's going to make our environment messier.

Oxygen

We know that the quality of the functionality in our bodily processes depends on the quality of the oxygen we get. We know that oxygen fuels the cells, optimises our brain and feeds our mitochondria to give us energy. It also does something to the body called alkalising. What do I mean by alkalising or alkalinity? The strength of alkalinity or acidity in a substance is measured on a PH scale, which stands for Potential of Hydrogen. The scale goes from 1 to 14: 0 to 1.69 is an acid, 7 is neutral, and 7.1 to 14 is alkaline. If we have lots of hydrogen ions in our body then our PH becomes highly acidic. A good example of an acidic liquid would be cola. A PH 7 is neutral and a good example of that is water. A PH value of 12 would be highly alkaline and an example of that would be soapy water.

If we want our bodily functions to be optimal then our PH value needs to be between 7.3 and 7.4 so moderately alkaline. Just like our internal body temperature needs to maintained at 37 degrees Celsius, our body needs to maintain a particular PH value and that may differ slightly in the body.

What happens when we subject ourselves to cold or hot environments? Our body has to use extra energy to compensate. It has to turn on its homeostatic functions in order to consistently facilitate that temperature. Our PH value acts the same way. If we're making our body highly acidic due to things like lack of oxygen, our body needs to use extra energy to over compensate in order to maintain a 7.3 PH value. Very often we can get very fatigued but also experience other symptoms like acid indigestion, arthritis, thrush, candida and much more.

Cancer cannot survive in alkaline environments. Dr Otto Heinrich Warburg won a Nobel Prize for proving that cancer is caused by a lack of oxygen to cells. This lack of oxygen forces cells to meet their needs through fermentation which can lead to cancer.

When we've been exercising really hard, we can enter an anaerobic state where the body uses a reserve of energy which is great for fight/flight situations. However when the body has run out of ATP (our bodies energy), lactic acid builds up in the body and this can feel quite painful as the body needs us to slow down. An extreme case of this is rigor mortis. 4-24 hours after the body dies, it begins to become extremely stiff. Why? Because without ATP the muscles contract.

When it comes to our sports performance, when we want to improve our endurance and lengthen the time that it takes for lactic acid to build in our body we need to stock up on ATP. What makes ATP? Our mitochondria. How do we fuel our mitochondria? Through oxygen!

If we want to improve the environment of our body then the first, easiest and quickest way is to increase our oxygen. Oxygen is life, oxygen is health, oxygen is alkaline, oxygen is energy. We're going to saturate our bodies with oxygen, increase our body's alkalinity, expand our lung capacity and optimise our brain cells, and if we want to – our endurance.

Because we are going to be raising the oxygen and decreasing the carbon dioxide in our body it's going to be completely normal to feel tingling sensations in our body, to feel pulsing and to feel lightheaded. Remember, what we're also doing by breathing is increasing our heart rate variability – this is going to change the electrical rhythms in our body too - allowing us to enter a much more peaceful state of mind.

This is a fantastic way to start every morning, just lying down in bed before you get up. We want to be breathing fully and deeply into our diaphragms, not our chest, and we can do it through our nose or mouth – whatever is most comfortable for you.

Yogis have been using breathing techniques for thousands of years to induce these altered states of consciousness. But what is actually happening in the brain at that moment? If we do these yogic and holotropic breathing sessions for long enough we'll start to increase the chemical in our brain dimethyltryptamine, also known as DMT or even referred to as the Spirit Molecule. When people have out of body and phenomenal spiritual experiences, DMT is the molecule that's being fired around in our brain. When you hear of people in South America drinking plant-based brews made by shamans giving them spirit walks – DMT is the active component. During longer holotropic/power breathing sessions you may find yourself having these wonderful yet peculiar experiences. As I've heard it phrased before "It's like getting high on your own supply". That's something you're more than welcome to give a go. The main reason we're doing these breathing exercises is because it's a great first step towards changing our biochemistry and functioning at a higher level throughout the day.

BREATHE Chapter Summary

- Within the autonomic nervous system we have the sympathetic nervous system (fight and flight response) and the parasympathetic nervous system (relax and recuperate). Each have an effect on breath, however by changing breathing consciously we can activate the different systems e.g. If we're feeling stressed (sympathetic) we can slow our breathing, focus on our exhales, and activate the parasympathetic nervous system to calm us down.

- Breathing affects our state which is made up of our physiology, our internal representations and our behaviour. By changing our posture we can change our mood. Physiology and emotions are also a bi-directional process.

- Most cases of back-pain are an evolutionary mismatch. By sitting in disempowering postures for long periods of time we cause the shape of our spines to change from a J shape (the shape we are born with) to an S shape.

- Energy is related directly to the quality of our mitochondria (quadrillion organelles that act as power plants converting oxygen and nutrients into energy).

- By not breathing into our diaphragm every breath we take could be up to 30% less effective. When we breathe it's important not to breathe into our chest but to breathe into our abdomen.

- Breathing acts as a pump for the lymph system, which is responsible for up to 70% of the removal of toxins in the body. It is vital we breathe deeply and effectively in order to optimise the function of this detox pump.

- Saturating our bodies with oxygen through deep and effective breathing can reduce lactic acid, increase the efficiency of our mitochondria and reduce our risk to disease.
- Doctor Otto Heinrich Warburg won a Nobel Prize for proving that cancer is caused by a lack of oxygen to cells. This lack of oxygen causes cells to meet their needs by fermentation, which can lead to cancer.

<u>MOVE</u>

"Move or die"

Ido Portal

Movement Vs Exercise

We have a very big problem in today's world... most of us have stopped moving. And, Oh My, have we suffered for it! When you look at all the species on the planet, we as homo sapiens could be classed as one of the best movers. You won't be able to find much competition in the animal kingdom when it comes to a species that can run long distances, sprint, climb trees, swim through oceans and ascend mountains quite like a human can.

It's due to our moving ability as well as our adaptable brains that we are be able to make homes on all terrains and in all climates. Whether it is Inuits living on the arctic circle or the Korowai people in Papa New Guinea who live in trees 140 feet high.

The average caveman would walk approximately 10 miles a day and the average cavewoman 6 miles a day. We have not evolved for a sedentary life. Every single thing our bodies do require movement: Our immune system, our reproductive facilities and our digestion all require us to move in order to function properly. Even our cells have specialised equipment inside them to detect our movement. It's one of the reasons why an astronaut's health will plummet the moment they leave the atmosphere. Just by removing gravity the sensitivity that our cells have of constantly moving against something has dissipated.

Remember at the beginning of the book when I discussed genes being turned on and turned off? One of the things that affect our very DNA is simply the way that we move. We see this in the rest of the animal kingdom all the time. If you've ever been to Sea World or seen killer whales in the wild you'll notice there will be a big difference between them. Killer whales in captivity have a collapsed dorsal fin whereas whales in the wild don't. By keeping a killer whale in a small enclosure and never allowing them to explore the breadth of the sea, their fin collapses.

The orca in captivity is very similar to ourselves. Simply by not actively moving and exploring our surroundings we're damaging our health right down to a genetic level. Now the reason I say movement and not exercise is because not only are they different but exercise also seems to contain a very negative connotation. People generally don't like exercise. How many people go to the gym for the first time, perhaps as part of a New Year's Resolution, go three or four times and give up? I can assure you it's the majority. In fact, most people give up their New Year's Resolutions to get fit by January 16th. Why do people negatively perceive exercise when we know deep down that we should be doing it?

Think about it. When we haven't moved our bodies in so long and then go to the gym or take part in intense exercise, what are the symptoms? Increased heart rate, sweaty palms, shortness of breath, lack of oxygen, change in blood supply... our body to some extent is mimicking a panic attack. Remember the quality of the emotional mind? It's not innovative. If for some reason or another it thinks you're in some sort of danger it will revert back to previous patterns of behaviour. Staying in bed yesterday didn't help my mind or body thrive but at least I survived, so I'm encouraged to do it again. That's the issue – most people associate exercise with pain, which we are hardwired to avoid.

When we're talking about movement and allowing our body to flourish we don't need to put our bodies into full blown panic attacks. Movement is simply to reap the non-exercise benefits of an activity. Walking a mile to the shops to get food, climbing a mountain to take in the beautiful view, stretching your legs and socialising with a friend. Exercise is movement, but because exercise is about reaping the physical benefits of movement, movement is not always exercise.

You may imagine exercise as going to the gym, lifting weights and cycling intensely etc. However, when we're talking about movement it can be as simple as getting up from your desk for a while, standing up for longer than usual, doing jumping jacks, using the stairs instead of the lift at the office. Timing in movement is vital, even if we are already in the habit of going to the gym and starting the day with intense exercise, by not moving throughout the rest of the day we are still living a sedentary lifestyle. What's better than walking 3 miles in the morning? Walking 1 mile at 3 separate points in the day.

Moving is a bit like food. If we were to have a weeks' worth of food all in one day and not eat again until the following week, this wouldn't be healthy for our bodies. To work optimally every day throughout the week we need to be nourishing our bodies daily. For our biomechanics to work optimally every day we need to be moving FREQUENTLY throughout the day. We already know what sitting down can do for our physiology but even cognitively our brain starts to make a dramatic shift when we sit. A part of our brain actually turns off.

Have you ever experienced sitting down comfortably and the phone rings and someone is telling you something very important? What do you do? 9/10 times you'll stand up and start pacing around. Why? Because you need to increase your cognitive functions. There are scientists who are producing more and more compelling research that shows movement or exercise is actually an even bigger benefit for our mind than it is our body.

Brain Before Your Body

If you are going to read any book about why to exercise and why to move; then read *The Spark* by John Ratey. He's an internationally renowned expert in neuropsychiatry and a clinical professor of psychiatry at Harvard Medical School. Hippocrates famously once said "If you're in a bad mood, walk. If you're still in a bad mood, walk again". The American Psychiatric Association has only recently caught up with this 2,000 years old advice and Ratey helps deliver the proof.

If we're not exercising and not moving our bodies we are 1.5x more likely to suffer from depression. In a landmark study at Duke University in 1999 James Blumenthal and his colleagues did a 16-week experiment where they randomly divided 156 patients suffering from depression into 3 groups. One group was prescribed the antidepressant Sertraline (commonly known as Zoloft), another was assigned a regular exercise routine, and the third was assigned both. In all 3 cases the group showed a significant drop in depression and about half of each group were in complete remission. Another 13% experienced fewer symptoms but didn't fully recover. Exercise was just as effective as an antidepressant. But the beauty of this is that there are 0 side effects and it's free.

So what sort of exercise was this group doing? Was it Crossfit? Spinning? Tri-athlete training? Not even close. All they had to do was walk or jog at 70-80% of their aerobic capacity for 30 minutes, plus a 10 minute warm up and 5 minute cooldown. They only had to do this 3 times per week. Think about it... just by moving their bodies every other day, their depression was significantly reduced or completely eliminated.

In terms of medication, Ratey explains that going for a run is like taking a little bit of Prozac and a little bit of Ritalin, because (like these drugs) exercise elevates the same neurotransmitters. A fairer description would be that exercise balances these neurotransmitters. By moving our bodies we are getting the same results without any side effects because our bodies have evolved to do this over the last 200,000 years!

If most people knew that exercising, even just on a minimum level, could work as affectively as Zoloft, imagine the size of the dent which could be created in the amount of people who are depressed! Sadly, because movement is free and easy it doesn't have a budget as big as the pharmaceutical companies.

Just by moving our bodies we are able to release a lovely cocktail of neurotransmitters that improves our wellbeing. The moment we stop so does that lovely cocktail. The best way I've heard this described was by Brian Johnson, CEO of Optimize: "There's days where I feel you couldn't pay me to exercise, but like many others I like feeling good way too much. And I know how I start to feel when I go without it. You shower everyday right? Well imagine if you decided you no longer need to shower, how do you think you're going to smell after a day, 3 days, a week? What about 6 months? Even after a few days without showering funnily enough not many people will still want to be around you. The exact same thing applies to exercise. If we're not moving consistently it's like you are not giving your insides a shower. And emotionally, psychologically, you start to smell".

Over 10,000 years ago no-one was told they had to exercise. Living in hunter-gatherer tribes movement was simply part of life. It is ingrained so heavily in our DNA to keep moving, especially when on the hunt for food. As our food is now all found in grocery stores we are creating an evolutionary mismatch again. We're disrupting that delicate biochemical sobriety that's been fined tuned for hundreds and thousands of years.

We know that if we want to get happy we move, but what if we want to get smarter? The quality of our learning and memory formation is dependent on the frequency and signalling activity throughout our neurons. By not exercising those connections our neural pathways can become eroded. Simply by exercising we have the ability to re-establish those connections. By moving regularly we increase the level of something called BDNF (Brain Derivative Neurotropic Factor). The moment we have an increase in BDNF that protein leads to the activation of signalling pathways that are responsible for our enhanced learning and memory. The best way to remember this is if we stop moving our brain starts to corrode and when we start moving our brain becomes rebooted. The erosion of neural-connections in our brain is synonymously linked with depression, so being able to re-establish those connections and enhancing our cognitive functions is a whole other way to help our wellbeing.

In Naperville Illinois an exercise class has completely changed the cognitive functions of local students. This is one of the few schools (less than 6%) that have a mandatory exercise period at the start of the day. The students are not graded on who is the fastest runner but rather they are graded on their effort and consistency. For example, in track running all the students are given heart rate monitors and are tasked with keeping their heart rate between 160 – 180 beats per minute and maintain this for 15 minutes. Similar to the depression study, this is approximately 75% of their aerobic capacity or maximum heart rate. The results? Not only are just 3% of the students overweight (compared to 30% of the country) but grades improved and this programme has turned these students into some of the smartest in the nation, ranking amongst the top in international standards tests.

It's not necessarily that exercise is making us smarter, it's more that it is charging up our brain so we are in an active state to receive and retain information more efficiently. A little bit like the Limitless pill (from the Bradley Cooper film), it didn't make anyone smarter – they were simply able to recall on the resources made available to them more effectively. If we want to increase our cognitive abilities as well as our happiness through the neurotransmitters previously mentioned, moving our bodies is absolutely essential.

The Best Exercise

What is the best exercise? Before I delve deeply into the answer, what would you guess to be the number one movement that not only helps reduce cholesterol and blood pressure, but also aids us in our biomechanics, aerobic capacity, and overall endurance and energy in our body?

That's right folks, walking! It doesn't matter how much exercise you are doing in the morning or evening, without walking we're dying. Move or die.

The best exercise is not a set movement, it is not a set regime, it is not a personal training plan... it is simply the one you're most likely to do again and again. On paper, what someone is telling you to do doesn't matter. It doesn't matter if you're focusing on compound exercises like a bench press, deadlift or squat. If you're not enjoying it and you are in no way encouraged to repeat this then it is pointless. No-one got fit from one workout, same as no-one got fat from eating one pizza. Remember what Aristotle said - we are what we **repeatedly** do. If we want to increase the health of our lives, not just our week, it has to be something we enjoy.

Even though three quarters of us cite our main reason for exercising as weight loss or better health, only one year down the line we are a 3rd more likely to quit than if we're simply exercising to create a sense of wellbeing and feeling centred.

Bit of a peculiar paradox, isn't it? That people who exercise for better health are the most likely to stop exercising overall. The reason we're moving *has* to be a compelling one, it has to be because we *enjoy* moving, not what moving is going to give us.

This life we have been given is a marathon and not a sprint. When we're playing a game that's long term why on earth would we use anything other than a long-term strategy?

In the Questions & Language section I asked the question "How is it I can look after my health better and enjoy every moment of it?". Let's ask ourselves a similar question now. What movement can I do alone or with friends that I would genuinely enjoy doing? You might surprise yourself, it may be as out there as tap dancing, climbing trees, or swimming in cold lakes. It doesn't matter because if you do anything you enjoy that is beneficial to your health your body will overcompensate and adapt to fit your new habits so that it becomes even easier for you to do it. I know this isn't a sexy answer – this isn't a short-cut to the six pack abs you may be looking for. But this isn't about being sexy, it is about being real and taking an approach that actually works. Don't get me wrong, you can kill yourself for 30 days and dramatically change your body, but this isn't the Primal Month Method... it's the Primal Life Method for a reason. We are not looking at increasing your lifespan, we are looking at increasing your health span. Let's not look at whether a programme can give us toned abs in 6 weeks. Wouldn't we rather take 2 years to get those abs and **keep them** for 30 years? Your choice of movement is a long-term investment. Remember the Primal Life motto: *enjoy* everything, need nothing. Not sacrifice everything, enjoy something.

Born To Run

I have mentioned a few times about endurance and energy and touched on the potential capabilities of our bodies. When we look at some of the physical feats that some humans have performed it's extraordinary. It really does seem super human. For example, how far do you think humans can run in one go? A marathon is 26.2 miles, an Ultraman is over 50 miles, but an incredible story that caught my eye is a tribe in Mexico called the Tarahumara who can run barefoot 150 – 200 miles in one go.

There is so much about our physiology that has evolved over 2 million years for us to perfectly run with great endurance and go the distance. A brilliant quality we possess is that we are incredible at sweating! When our body starts to overheat, unlike many quadruped mammals, we can cool our bodies down without stopping. Every pore in our body can secrete micro molecules of liquid so that when they evaporate we cool down, that's what sweating is. Unlike dogs who can't do this simultaneously, we can control our heat while moving. The only way a dog can reduce its temperature is through panting and it cannot pant while it runs. Despite them being able to run faster than us over short distances, we would always catch up to them because we can go the distance. And that's not just for dogs. With horses we all have the capability to undertake a marathon quicker than them because of their need to control their heat through breathing.

As we now know, we have had the same body for the last 200,000 years and are all part of the same species that's been around for 2 million years. Our earliest fossils can be found in the fertile crescent and much of our time as this species was spent in the plains of the Savannah. As the climate changed and forests began to disappear there would be empty plains and long grass between them. This caused us to move over hundreds of thousands of years from quadrupeds (on all fours) to bipedal movers (two legs). This would allow us to see any predators over the long grass. What it also did was allow us to radiate heat more effectively through our body. By being bipedal movers we were able to expend less calories per mile than any quadrupeds, including our primate relatives. On less food we could move further. These journeys could be dangerous running across the plains, not knowing what predators were around. We are the descendants of the genes that were strong enough, fast enough, and had the endurance to survive that danger.

A big part of our diet during the Savannah hunting times would have involved meat, usually by hunting animals much larger than ourselves. However there is no evidence to suggest we were using tools for this more than 300,000 years ago. So how is it that as a pack of homo sapiens we were able to survive eating animals much quicker and stronger than ourselves?

In long distance running men and women hold an extremely close gap of athletic performance, unlike most other sports. Now here's a really incredible fact about running: the University of Utah did a research study where they tracked the progression of marathon times over the course of male and female runners lives. The conclusion they reached was that if you started running a marathon at age 19 and kept training then you'd become quicker and quicker every year until you peaked at an average age of 27. Slowly your time would drop back to the same speed you were running at when 19 years old. Now that seems quite obvious, doesn't it? Of course after a certain age the level of your running is going to start decreasing to the level you were at originally. Most people would guess that would take perhaps 8-10 years after hitting their peak; in your late 30s you'd be back to where you started. Nope. It actually takes 45 years! 64-year-old men and women are running marathons at the same speed as teenagers.

There are particular theories that are based around why we seem to be born to run. Why is it that even people in their 60s can run the same speed as teenagers? Why is it that women can run the same speed and have the same endurance as men? In short, it's because we went hunting as a pack. The best way to describe our species (homo sapiens) especially more than 2,0000 years ago, is that we were **wild** and depended on each other to survive. Like a pack of wolves we would need to hunt together in order to gather enough food for everyone. We were hunter gatherer nomads and didn't have many possessions, we'd simply move where the food moved. This required all of us. The older men who'd been hunting the longest would be the best teachers, the 19-year olds would be the students learning to hunt and the middle age men would be ready to make the actual kill as they'd be the most effective.

The two times we most need animal proteins in our lives is when we're an adolescent and a nursing mother. It is pointless for 27-year olds to be many miles away when the people who need that protein the most are back in a camp – so everyone, including women, would keep the same fast pace. The same especially goes for the older runners – these men would be the expert trackers, knowing which antelope to pick out etc. It wouldn't be helpful if they were 10-15 miles behind everyone else. But like I questioned earlier, what were we doing and how were we killing bigger and faster animals when we didn't have weapons? It was our endurance. By being able to chase animals over extreme long distances as a pack we were able to run that animal to exhaustion.

Another reason we were born to run is that it feels good. 'Runners high' is a well-documented experience. Remember, we get rewarded when we carry out certain evolutionary processes. When we are running we release a series of endocannabinoids which are the same chemicals released when people smoke marijuana. Running also increases the number of receptors for those endocannabinoids, so not only do we release a flurry of chemicals that feel good but by having more receptors we can feel an even stronger high.

I used to hate the idea of running. In fact, my sister never lets me live it down. When we were younger my dad tried to take my sister and I out for a run. Even though I was 10 years old, just over 1 mile in I started crying. Now when I bring running up amongst my family I simply get responded with "*mock cries* Oh, I can't make it Dad".

Something that has become popularised over recent years is barefoot running. If you talk to anyone for more than 30 seconds about running it is not long before injuries are mentioned. We seem to have this mismatch between the rest of our body being built for distance, yet the moment anyone in western society starts running they get injured. The theory behind this is simple: we are wearing shoes, something again unbeknown to our genes. Our feet have evolved to do 1 thing - keep our balance via interacting with the ground. Over time we have introduced a middleman – the shoe. Suddenly our feet are no longer grounded and so instead of our body adjusting to a mixture of terrains over the decades, our feet have become restricted. Just like sitting down, the rest of our body structure has to adapt, which can of course create negative symptoms. It is yet another evolutionary mismatch. Instead of looking at the primary cause, like with most illnesses, we get out the Ibuprofen, the Deep Heat, the Deep Freeze and we treat the symptoms and not the source. Pain isn't something that should be masked, it's something that should be listened to. If we don't listen to the message the first time it'll find a stronger and more noticeable way to deliver it to us (which could be putting your knees out of action), all because we've changed the mechanics of our body for too long.

Strength

My favourite description of strength is by the author and personal trainer Shawn Phillips. He describes strength not just as the absence of disease but "the presence of abundant energy - a compacity and reserve to be a force in your world. It's inclusive of health and at the same time so much more. It's being healthy and flowing with energy, power and confidence."

When we think about strength we shouldn't just think about it in its physical capacity. We can also see strength as that emotional reserve that acts as a fuel for an extraordinary life.

Building strength physically and emotionally are things I've briefly touched upon but it includes a key component, usually referred to as the Training Effect. The Training Effect in its physical capacity is when our body leads to an improvement as a reaction to adaptive responses. In short, the only reason we're ever going to get our body to change is if we give it a big enough reason to change. Our bodies won't get stronger if we're doing resistance training that isn't challenging enough for us. When asked how many sit-ups he could do, Muhammad Ali once famously replied "I don't count my sit-ups, I only start counting when it starts hurting, because they're the only ones that count". This means if we are lifting weights the training only starts when the pain shows up. What so many of us do when we are weight/resistance training is we slow down the moment the body feels that discomfort. Because we haven't given our bodies that reason to change we keep going back to the gym only to see little results in our improvement and therefore stop. If I was doing anything where I thought I was working hard but didn't see any change, I'd probably give up too.

The Primal Life Method isn't a personal training course so I won't be going into details to get your body shredded or toned. However, what we must understand is that in building strength physically or emotionally, we need to leave our comfort zone.

As a friend once told me "The comfort zone is a fantastic place, beautiful, but nothing ever grows there".

Weight training and working our muscles for men and women has incredible health effects, one of which is increasing bone density. One of the greatest ways we can reduce bone loss as we age is to simply add strength training into part of our weekly practice. It increases the strength of connective tissue like our tendons and that leads to improved motor function and reduces the risk of injury.

We need to be training our muscles a minimum of 2 times per week. Age has proved to no longer be an excuse for how strong we want to be in our life. In fact, the Noll Laboratory for Human Performance compared young men with men between ages 45 – 60 and found that aerobic capacity, along with other factors like percentage of body fat, was not at all correlated with their age but with the amount of time they spent training their body. The Human Nutrition Centre on Aging found muscle growth in people ranging from 66 – 90 was again the same as young people who did the same amount of training on their bodies. As we discovered in the 'Born To Run' section, we all have peak ages, but this shows us that our capacity for fitness doesn't change with age, only the amount of time we are willing to spend training. With X-Rays we can see that the bone density and muscle health of a 35 year old triathlete can be identical to a 75 year old triathlete. If you compared the X-Ray of a 35 year old sedentary person with that of the 75 year old triathlete, you'd likely think they had been mistakenly swapped. We only have to turn on the TV once a year and watch the marathon to see that older and older people are still able to cross that finish line. In today's world it seems that 80 and 90 year olds are exploring their physical capabilities and succeeding to do things that many 20 somethings can't do. It is never too late to start this process. Life is a marathon not a sprint. The potential we have as humans to increase our health span is phenomenal. Not many people look forward to the idea of being over 60, but I have friends in the 60+ age bracket who are fitter and healthier than most people I know in their 20s and filled with so much more experience. Getting older is something to look forward to, not something to shy away from. As we all know it's coming to us anyway. This is just another fact that allows us to enjoy this journey further.

If we look at strength in the emotional realm we have to keep bringing awareness to the fact that training our emotions, and our capacity to grow intellectually is identical to the Training Effect in our muscles. One of the greatest muscles we can grow emotionally is courage. Just to clarify, courage is never about the absence of fear, it's about the ability to feel the fear but do it anyway. When we face fear (physically or mentally) something extraordinary happens in our growth. This something is usually referred to as the Control Constant Matrix (CCM). The CCM states that if I complete a goal or face a fear that was a 7/10 for me in one area of my life, then as a by-product of facing that fear I will also complete a goal or face a fear that's 7/10 in another area of my life. We see this all the time. If someone loses weight and gets the body they want, naturally their confidence increases. By facing the fear of going to the gym they're able to start talking to strangers for the first time in a confident manner. The moment someone gets the relationship they've always wanted at the same time they effortlessly stop smoking. It means that if I want to increase my bubble of growth to a larger concentric circle, then the moment I move to a bigger circle my life will change holistically and everything in that circle will become bigger. The Miracle Question is a perfect way to take baby steps in moving to bigger circles and expanding the capabilities of who we are.

Some of us, on purpose or by accident, might find ourselves facing a fear of extraordinary proportion. Instead of jumping to one slightly bigger circle, we've jumped 3 circles ahead. A

wonderful example is from one of my seminars I was teaching...
There was a lady who suffered greatly from social anxiety and
she was on medication for this. Logically she understood the
idea of breaking through her comfort zone, but like most of us,
putting it into practice was a different matter altogether. After
all, facing fear is terrifying, an obvious fact we often forget. I
was talking to her about the idea of what it would be like if she
were to just go outside and lie down on the sidewalk and not
talk to anyone. We spoke and laughed together about how
great that would be, coming out of her comfort zone etc. What
she didn't expect was when I said "ok, that's exactly what we're
going to do!". What do you think happened next? It wasn't a
logical idea anymore, it became reality for her. At first she was
terrified, the amygdala in her limbic system kicked in and
suddenly she started feeling fear. "What if people laugh at me?"
"People will think I'm being silly"... and suddenly this wave of
excuses came out as to why she couldn't do it and why it would
be a bad idea. The amygdala can't make us do anything that we
don't want to do, but it can offer some marvellous propaganda.
Even though she knew logically what was happening (as we'd
been talking about the emotional mind) this of course didn't
make the fear less severe, it was still very real to her.

Eventually she was persuaded and at one point she laid down
on the sidewalk and stayed even once I'd left her there. Within
10 seconds of her lying down something spectacular had
happened - she realised it wasn't anywhere near as bad as she'd
imagined. She actually found it really comfortable. All that fear
was self-imposed and she broke through it. I found out the next
day that after talking to her doctor she gave up her medication
for social anxiety, something she'd been wanting to do for a
while. By confronting an extreme fear that took her completely
out the comfort zone a by-product was made that meant she
was able to complete another incredible feat overnight.

Another way to think about it is like this... The speed of my growth is dependent on my frequency and willingness to experience discomfort. You can see why courage is one of the greatest muscles we have to increase our overall strength as a person.

MOVE Chapter Summary

- The way that we move and exercise can switch on and off certain genes.
- Orcas bred in captivity have collapsed dorsal fins, something you will not see in wild orcas due to their ability to move around freely.
- Movement and exercise are not the same thing. Exercise is about reaping the physical benefits of movement, while movement is done to reap the non-exercise benefits of an activity.
- It's important we move frequently throughout the day as opposed to moving intensely for one period of time in a day.
- Exercise is intimately linked with our happiness and cognitive wellbeing. If we don't exercise we are 1.5x more likely to be depressed. Experiments have shown that minimal exercise has the same pharmacological benefits as some anti-depressants. Exercise is "like taking a little bit of Prozac, a little bit of Ritalin", as it stimulates the same neurotransmitters.
- Movement increases intelligence and increases the protein BDNF in our brain. This leads to the activation of signalling pathways which are responsible for enhanced learning and memory. If we stop moving and lead a sedentary life those neural connections can begin to erode. The erosion of neural connections is synonymously linked with depression.
- The best exercise is the one we're most likely to do again. Studies show that if our main reason for exercising is weight loss or better health we're 3x more

likely to quit than if we exercise to create a sense of wellbeing and feeling centred (we enjoy it).

- Exercise and movement should be done sustainably so that we don't only get the results we want in our body but we keep those results.
- Due to our ability to control our heat while moving as well as burning fats for fuel, as bipedal movers we are built for endurance and over 300,000 years ago we would hunt by running animals to exhaustion together as a pack over 30+ miles.
- Tribes like the Tarahumara can barefoot run 150-200 miles at once due to their ability to tap into their evolutionary legacy.
- Shoes are an evolutionary mismatch that can cause many injuries because we have been forced to change our overall posture because our feet are no longer in connection with the ground.
- To build strength our body can go under a response called the Training Effect. This is where our muscles and body lead to an improvement as a reaction to adaptive responses.
- Aerobic capacity, percentage of body fat and muscle growth are not correlated with age but are with training frequency.
- Strength training increases bone density and strengthens the connective tissue like tendons that lead to improved motor function and reduced risk of injury.
- The strength and growth of our emotional capabilities is dependent on our frequency and willingness to experience discomfort.

FUEL

"Our bodies are beautifully designed to handle all kinds of stress; but our genes have to be working; they have to have the right nutrients"

Dr Rhonda Patrick

Diets Don't Work

It seems fairly obvious that the food we eat should affect our performance somehow. If we imagine ourselves as a racing car, by changing the way we think it's like getting the best driver behind the wheel. Breathing consciously is like adding a Nitrous Oxide Tank to give us the needed boost. By taking the car around the race track regularly and moving it we're making sure it doesn't rust or break. We could have the greatest racing car and driver on the planet at this point but we're not even going to make it off the start line if we haven't filled it up with the right fuel. You can put vodka in a Ferrari and it will still go around a track – just not very well. Our bodies are the same.

Statistically more people die from obesity than they do from starvation. We have been fuelling our bodies with too much poison and as a result it has started to break down early on us. Despite this chapter being about nutrition, this is not a diet book for multiple reasons: 1) Diets don't work, 2) I am not a dietician, 3) There is not a universal diet that works for everyone. I will delve into these points in more detail throughout the chapter, but for us to feel biochemically sober and start a path that will lead us to our peak, covering the fundamentals of nutrition is essential. It doesn't matter how positive our thinking is, if we haven't supplied our body with the right energy to get out of bed it's the greatest limitation we could put on exploring our potential.

Diets do not work, simple. If we're going on a diet it suggests that at some point we must come off it. The average person when coming off a diet not only goes back to their original weight, but gains an extra 2lbs of body fat. The only thing that diets can truly guarantee us is a way to gain unwanted excess weight. Diets scream deprivation. The moment our body feels its somehow deprived of something, the emotional mind becomes more vigilant than ever before. It believes we are doing something to threaten our survival, such as entering a state of pain and avoiding all pleasure. Unless we are looking to only lose weight on a very temporary basis, e.g. for a photoshoot or beach holiday, diets themselves are nonsensical. Even if we have the willpower to get to our goal weight, in our minds we have set ourselves up only for a temporary habit. Many people who are successful on diets, whether that's through taking shakes or never eating their favourite foods, often fall to the illusion that by coming off the diet at their goal weight and going back to their old eating habits that they'll somehow stay the same weight. We know this is impossible. When it comes to the first change in our habit towards the fuel we put in our body it must be this: I will not change to an eating habit unless I thoroughly believe I can do it for the rest of my life. Just like in the 'Best Exercise' we want to treat fuel like a long-term game. Putting ourselves into a sense of restriction is only going to make us suffer mentally. Remember the hormone cortisol? If we're feeling stressed (which will likely occur on a diet), cortisol acts as a survival mechanism and holds onto our bodily fat... because fat is a great storage for fuel and if we're in fight/flight mode our body doesn't know when we're next going to eat. Therefore, if we make a change in our eating, it has to be something we enjoy. We're not looking to get the perfect body in 6 weeks, it doesn't even matter if we don't get it in 2 years, what matters is that if we do get it that we're able to keep it.

When it comes to the topic of nutrition there could not be more controversy in the scientific field. Something that's so vital to our life that we've been doing for the last 2 million years as a species, you'd think we'd have sussed it out by now! How is it that 2 doctors in the same field, equally qualified, can be saying the exact opposites when it comes to the quality of our diet? Something we must understand when it comes to our nutrition is that there is no one diet plan out there for the world.

If we really want to know the best diet for us then we should get ourselves tested. The standard test that most physicians give simply identifies the absence of disease as opposed to optimum health. By taking the following tests we can delve under the skin as to what is really happening in our unique body:

Complete Blood Count of Red Blood Cells (RBCs) and White Blood Cells (WBCs)	Cyrex Labs Assays (the most accurate way to test for food allergies)	IGF-1 (Growth Hormone Surrogate)
Total Iron Binding Capacity	Dehydroepiandrosterone Sulfate (DHEA)	Metabolic Hormones Cortisol (Blood)
SHBG	Gut Test	SHBG
Estradiol	DNA Test	Insulin 7
Vitamin B12	RBC Magnesium	Testosterone
Folate	Hormones	Free Testosterone
Blood Lipids	TSH	Albumin
HDL	Glucose	Total Protein
LDL	HbA1c	Vitamin D
Triglycerides	Liver & Kidney Health	Calcium
Lp(s)	BUN	Sodium
ApoB	AST	Potassium
Basic Inflammation	Creatinine	Chloride
hs-CRP	ALT	Carbon Dioxide
Thyroid & Blood Sugar	Total Bilirubin 6	Ferritin (Serum)

Once we have accurate measurements to where we are we have a terrific starting point that we can then take to a dietician who can give us the bespoke strategy we need to prime our bodies with the right fuel. No-one can tell you what the best diet for you is, until they can objectively see the internal measurements of your health. Some people thrive on a vegan diet, whilst others can get the same results through a paleo diet. We're all unique; this chapter is about finding out what's best for you and then being able to implement that.

The key point I'll be discussing throughout this chapter is how vital our fuel is for our happiness. Fuel doesn't just affect our physical health, it is without a doubt connected to our emotional wellbeing too.

The Second Brain

Our brain is intimately linked with the way we think and feel. We prioritise our brain when it comes to our emotional wellbeing, however the organ that is just as important as this which we often forget about is the gut, which is often referred to as The Second Brain due to the extraordinary number of neurons this organ possesses.

As well as the brain, the gut helps regulate immune cells, hormones and muscles. But here's the real reason why our gut is the most vital key when it comes to opening the potential of our happiness. When I first spoke about The Happy Caveman releasing neurotransmitters in the heart, brain and gut what I didn't mention is that an estimated 80-90% of the serotonin that's released in our body is manufactured in our gut. Is it really any surprise that our dietary choices have an impact on our mood? Some neurologists and psychiatrists are often finding that antidepressants can be less effective in treating depression than dietary changes. Some research is even showing that our 'second brain' may not be so secondary at all, as the gut can act independently from our brain and control multiple functions separately from our brain's control.

This is just another example of how our thoughts and feelings are a complete bi-directional process. Our thoughts do not just affect our feelings, our feelings are affecting our thoughts. We often say out loud that we have 'a gut feeling' about something and by understanding that this organ can work independently and is responsible for the majority of our 'good feelings' we can see that looking after the quality of our gut is crucial to accessing a better state of happiness.

Our gut has its own immune system referred to as gut-associated lymphatic tissue (GALT) and this represents 70-80%

of our bodies total immune system. If we're not looking after our gut it means we're not looking after our entire body. Other than the skin the gut is the most likely organ to encounter foreign organisms and therefore if there are issues and has sensed foreign pathogens, it is able to communicate this 'gut feeling' with every other immune system cell in the body. It's the doorman of a club, consistently on guard and communicating with the club manager and staff on the club floor, to provide updates on the health and safety of the situation.

Due to the unexpected volume of toxic foods we are consistently eating we are causing our gut to become inflamed. This sends stress signals across our immune and nervous systems and more importantly it will transmit a signal through something called the vagus nerve, eventually getting picked up by our brain.

According to David Perlmutter (the only medical doctor in the USA who is both a board-certified neurologist and a member of the American College of Nutrition), "all degenerative conditions are inflammation." These include conditions such as asthma, chronic peptic ulcers, sinusitis. More seriously, inflammation can also lead to brain disorders such as dementia, Alzheimer's and strokes. 70% of all deaths in the USA can be accounted for by cardiovascular diseases, cancers and diabetes. The link that binds all of them? Inflammation.

Very often when an organ is experiencing severe stress it can send a pain signal, after all digestive disorders are much easier to recognise as we experience bloating, pain, constipation and gas etc. The brain however being a much more elusive organ makes it harder to spot inflammation or stress until it's often too late.

If you're feeling mental fatigue or brain fog often, it is a sign of inflammation that if unchecked could leader to problems later on down the line.

Inflammation, just like cortisol, is actually a great process in small doses. It's part of your body's response to an invasion of toxins or any damage on its cells – it's not the disease, it's the cure. The process involves a production of white blood cells that can protect us from infection from foreign organisms like bacteria and viruses. In some diseases the immune system can trigger an inflammatory response even when there's no foreign pathogens that these cells need to kill. In these cases, the white blood cells begin to cause damage to healthy tissues, destroying the body while believing it's still fighting off these viruses. While this is happening the body's normal immune and metabolic processes get suspended as the primary infection is being dealt with. You can see that long-term inflammation will certainly cause chronic conditions to worsen and the body to deteriorate.

By eating a large array of foods that contain inflammatory agents it can cause us (our gut) to suffer from chronic inflammation which restricts the guts ability to manufacture serotonin for the body, giving us the happy feeling we want to experience day to day. Depression can in essence be gut inflammation! Dr David Perlmutter goes as far to say "Depression isn't a chemical imbalance in the brain, it's inflammation". If we have been feeling numb and low for a while and can't explain why, it's time to look at what fuel we've been feeding our gut (another reason to get a gut test).

Something very often ignored when it comes to our gut health is our gut microbiome (the community of bacteria that lines the gut). To give you a perspective on how powerful the collection of these bacteria can be in the realms of our mental health, studies with mice that have been genetically altered to have no gut bacteria all showed signs of acute anxiety, the inability to handle stress as well as lower levels of BDNF (see MOVE chapter), as well as having gut inflammation. However, once the mice were fed with a diet rich in probiotics all these symptoms were reversed.

To take this a step further, a 2013 experiment found in the Journal of Gastroenterology recalls how a team of UCLA researchers showed that bacteria can affect brain function in humans through the consumption of foods. They split participants into three groups, giving:

Group 1: A yoghurt mixture containing several probiotics to be taken twice a day

Group 2: A yoghurt mixture with no bacteria

Group 3: No yoghurt or probiotics at all

The results... Under a functional MRI machine (a machine that shows brain activity – technically referred to as 'excitability'), 4 weeks from the start of the experiment, all the participants were shown a mixture of images designed to induce a negative emotional response. All the participants who ate the probiotic yoghurt showed decreased activity in both the insula and the somatosensory cortex when being shown the emotionally inducing images. The way their brain was responding to negative activity was different than prior to eating the probiotic yoghurt. On a neurological level, just by changing the gut microbiome these participant's reality had changed. Changing our fuel in a sense becomes a biochemical hack for altering our map of the world. If you feel yourself reacting to events more negatively than you'd like then look after your gut microbiome. Change your gut microbiome and you change your reality!

Poisons

This is the first and only time throughout this book I'll be putting the focus on what not to do! The reason for this is because when talking about the food/fuel we're putting in our body, and how it affects our health, what we stop eating has a much bigger impact on our health than what we decide to start eating. It doesn't matter how much broccoli you've eaten, if you're walking through the woods and eat poison berries then you're still going to die.

If we want to alter our diet for a healthier lifestyle but are still regularly digesting foods that aren't good for us, our health is still likely to diminish. In this section I want to discuss poisons that we must avoid to be living with optimal health. It's very likely you'll know this on a logical level, but your emotional mind doesn't. Let's go into more detail to really understand what's happening to your health and happiness if you're ingesting these poisons on a daily basis.

Sugar

Sugar tastes great. Who doesn't love a sweet dish? Even after a beautiful big Christmas meal when we can't move, who could even dream of turning away the delicious dessert that follows? But why do we love sugar so much?

In our brain we possess a region called the nucleus accumbens, the absolute centre for the reward circuitry. If this part of the brain on a functional MRI scan is lighting up it means we're having a darn good time - alcohol, tobacco and cocaine all hit this sweet spot. Alongside this so does sugar and processed carbohydrates. It isn't necessarily because it 'tastes so good' but rather because we are shooting fireworks upstairs. This has been tested in the American Journal of Clinical Nutrition using milkshakes of the same consistency, sweetness and caloric/nutrient value. One used corn syrup (a processed sugar and fast acting carbohydrate) and another used uncooked corn starch (a slow acting carbohydrate). Despite them having the same taste, the participants who consumed the corn syrup milkshake (due to a lit up nucleus accumbens and a sharper spike/drop of blood sugar) reported to be hungrier quicker and craving more than the participants who consumed the uncooked starch shake. It's another reason most diets do not work for people. If we're eating less but still eating sugar and processed carbohydrates, we're still activating this part of the brain. By feeling hungry and having the nucleus accumbens ready for another hit, our willpower is only going to erode over time.

There is a benefit to wanting sugar the way we do. When our caveman bodies can taste that there is sugar in a food, e.g. fruits and honey, our taste buds can detect the glucose (sugar) within those foods which in turn sends the signal to our brain that we have in front of us a calorie dense food which will give us the source of energy we need. In a hunter gatherer life, coming across a calorie dense food would be rare and celebrated. After all, we would have no idea when we would next be eating – so we should stock up for the winter! Glucose is a terrific first line energy source! If we don't use all the glucose available in that meal then (due to high levels of glucose being toxic to the body) insulin acts as a key to unzip fat cells and move the unused sugar into a fat cell where it is stored until it's needed again. Unused sugar turns into fat. Fat is just energy available to us that hasn't been used yet. We want plenty of fat if our survival is being threatened. Just to give you an idea of how much unused energy the average person has available to them: immediate sugar in the average body equates to approximately 5,000 calories while the energy we have available in fat equates to approximately 140,000 calories! Can you see the evolutionary mismatch we have coming our way? Imagine we take those cavemen who react to sugar that way and give them a device that at a push of a button can order calorie dense food to their door (they don't even have to move). As a bonus, when eaten, it lights up the nucleus accumbens so they are experiencing fireworks of a pleasure. Then as an extra, give them a device like a TV which puts them into a trance so they don't even eat mindfully. What do you think would happen to that caveman? You can see why obesity is at an all time high on a global scale - we have 2 million year old caveman technology in our brains working in a modern-day lifestyle. When people say they have a problem with food, a food addiction, they couldn't be further from the truth! It's not a problem with food people have, it's a problem with sugar and processed carbohydrates. Give me a great example of someone who became obese from eating too many vegetables and I can give you a great example of someone who lies!

But surely calories are all equal? If I burn off more calories than I eat then isn't that a recipe for successful weight loss? Calories in a vacuum are equal yes, however our bodies are not vacuums. A study done by Kekwick and Pawan (1956) showed that when applying calorie restricted diet of 1,000cals to 3 groups of participants, simply by varying their macronutrients, the weight lost varied greatly between them. The average weight lost when 90% of the diet was fat equated to 0.9lbs per day. When 90% Protein it was 0.6lbs per day. However, having a calorie restricted diet of 1,000cals eating 90% carbohydrates led to 0.24lbs of weight gain per day! Even when eating 50% of the recommended daily allowance, participants eating 90% carbohydrates still gained weight! Not only that but cravings and hunger are a signal usually sent when our blood sugar is dipping dramatically, something that is less likely to happen when eating high fat. So, these participants eating high carbohydrates would have felt hunger more frequently than the other 2 groups while gaining weight. What a painful process!

Let's look at some other illnesses that sugar does to our body other than make us over weight. This has been taken from Nancy Appleton's *Lick the Sugar Habit*.

- Sugar can suppress the immune system

- Sugar feeds cancer cells and has been linked to breast, ovarian, prostate and rectal cancer

- Sugar can weaken eyesight and cause premature skin aging

- Sugar can cause premature aging in general and increase your risk of Alzheimer's disease

- Sugar can cause auto immune disease, arthritis, asthma, heart disease, migraines and multiple sclerosis (sugar causes inflammation!!)

We're eating 5x the amount of sugar on a daily basis than our grandparents were and our health is suffering for it. By overloading our body and giving it too much sugar to process, our mitochondria (the powerplants that act as energy factories) begin to burn out and die in the pancreas cells, our cells can no longer process the sugars and become resistant to the hormone insulin (key for moving sugar into fat) and they back up in the blood becoming toxic which can lead to diseases like diabetes. What's better than tackling the symptoms? It's tackling the source! But what's even better than tackling the source? Preventing the problem from ever happening in the first place! It is by far the number one most poisonous substance found in foods that we must eliminate if we want to strengthen our gut as well as our immune system and overall health and sense of well-being.

All foods can be measured on something called the Glycemic Index (GI). The Glycemic Index is a numerical reflection of how the carbohydrate within a food affects our blood glucose (sugar) levels. The numbers rank 0-100. Foods with a GI over 55 (High GI) will show high fluctuations in the blood as it is rapidly digested, absorbed and metabolised in the blood. Low GI foods produce far smaller fluctuations in the blood glucose and insulin levels allowing people to experience less cravings in their hunger and more stable energy throughout the day. When sugar is absorbed and metabolised quickly it can cause a large drop in the glucose levels (often lower than before the food was first eaten). This causes crashes in energy. So, here is a little test. Out of the following foods which do you think has the highest GI - the biggest sugar rush?

1. A slice of whole wheat bread

2. Snickers bar

3. A banana

4. A tablespoon of sugar

Ok, is this a trick question? Is the answer staring you in the face? Is it table sugar with a GI of 68? You could be right as that is higher than the snickers bar. The banana is indeed the lowest of the 4. It is in fact the slice of wholemeal bread with a GI of 71! It goes against common sense... how can wholemeal bread be higher in its sugar spike on my body than table sugar? Wholemeal bread actually has the same GI as white bread. There's not a large list of foods that give our blood glucose levels a higher surge than wheat! And that smoothly brings me onto the next poison...

<u>Grains</u>

Whole wheat, multigrain, seven-grain, live grain and stone ground grains are all very common and often referred to as healthy choices. Despite eating these foods as a society for the last 10,000 years, this is but a blink on our evolutionary timeline and any change in our DNA is negligible. Our genes are responsible for how we process the foods we eat and only in the last 5% of our genetic history have we introduced grains into our diet. Something I need to stress on top of this is that the majority of wheat we eat today has gone through modern hybridisation and GM technology. If there were any natural strains of grain that our hunter gatherer ancestors came across, it certainly wouldn't be genetically, chemically or structurally similar to the 133lbs of wheat that the average American consumes every year.

Gluten is a protein that makes up the majority of wheat protein. When the word gluten is mentioned we tend to think of the small percentage of people with celiac disease (an auto immune disease). It only affects about 0.4-0.8% of the population in the United States but causes gut inflammation in over 80% of people! If we want to poison our brain, then gluten is a perfect way to do that. Any high carbohydrate diet is one of the most prominent ways to stimulate the inflammatory pathways that reach the brain. A study at the University of Wales and in Toronto showed that cognitive functions in students such as verbal memory performance, working memory, selective attention and executive function were all worse after eating fast digesting carbohydrates compared to slower carbs (Low GI).

Being able to recognise that our brain is in trouble is a very difficult task, so it's really important we are mindful when we are eating our foods. Do you feel tired or can't concentrate after that big lunch? It's a sign that your body is having difficulty processing that fuel. It's a sign that our diet is not working for us! If we are to go back to our gut microbiome, the two things that do the most damage are gluten and manufactured fructose (corn syrup – processed sugar). We want to stay away from the High GI carbohydrates that give us inflammation, hunger cravings and ruin our cognitive function. Consider grain as the new alcohol, taking you away from biochemical sobriety.

Dairy

We have a dairy myth in our society that really started to take off during successful marketing campaigns such as "Milk does the body good". Drinking milk is associated with strong bones due to good levels of calcium, however this couldn't be further from the truth. Dr John McDougall, an American physician, has scoured medical literature and not found one case study relating to someone who has ever had a deficiency in calcium providing they were eating enough calories. It could be said that the consumption of dairy and weak bones forms a stronger link together. The countries with the highest dairy consumption including USA, UK, Sweden and New Zealand also share the highest rates of osteoporosis. Countries like China that consume just a third the amount of dairy have next to no cases – yet they are still getting more than enough calcium through plant-based diets. By reducing the level of animal proteins in dairy that are leaching calcium from the bones they are left with a net surplus, unlike the other countries mentioned.

Just like industrialised grains and fast acting carbohydrates (such as manufactured fructose), dairy (milk and cheese) was not part of our primal eating until approximately 7,500 years ago when we began as a species to rear animals. Again, that's a fraction of the time we have had for our genes to adjust to a new way of processing these foods. The ability to drink milk comes from a gene found in mammals called LCT which creates an enzyme lactase, a protein that digests the lactose sugar found in milk. After infancy this gene switches off for most mammals. In a minority of humans, LCT gene mutations can be found leaving the gene switched on allowing them to be able to digest milk appropriately into adulthood. However, this means that a large group of the human population is actually lactose intolerant. Being lactose intolerant doesn't mean you die on a sip of milk, it just means your body is having difficulty digesting it. Just like with wheat though, we may not always get the strongest symptoms to show us this is the case (another reason for a DNA test when coming to diet). Either way humans seem to be the only species that habitually drinks another species milk, and certainly the only species that continues to drink milk after infancy! My favourite quote about dairy comes from Dr Michael Klaper who became well known from his popular documentary *Cowspiracy*.

> *"I did much of my growing up on a dairy farm in northern Wisconsin. I began milking cows when I was 8 years old. Several things are now clear to me: The purpose of cow's milk is to turn a 65-pound calf into a 700-pound cow as rapidly as possible. Cow milk IS baby calf growth fluid. No matter what you do to it, that is what the stuff is. Everything in that white liquid – the hormones, the lipids, the proteins, the sodium, the growth factors like IGF-I – are all there to start that calf growing into a great big cow, or else they would not be there. Whether you pour it on your cereal as a liquid, churn it into butter, curdle it into yogurt, ferment it into cheese, or add sugar and freeze it to make ice cream... it's still baby calf growth fluid! Its sole purpose is to increase weight and promote growth in tissues throughout the mammalian body. It's great stuff if you are a baby calf, but if you are a human trying to create a lean and healthy body it will NOT "do the body good."*

Dr Klaper goes on to cite a research paper from Japan that confirms estrogen (the primary female sex hormone) is successfully absorbed into the body after drinking milk and testosterone is decreased. Researchers go on to say that sexual maturation in pre-pubescent children could be negatively affected by drinking ordinary intakes of cow's milk.

As a logical argument, removing dairy from our diet makes sense. What else is milk from mammals but a medium to transport the hormones and chemical components needed to make that specific mammal grow? One of the hormones already mentioned by Dr Klaper is Insulin Growth Factor 1 (IGF-1). IGF-1 levels are strongly linked to prostate, lung and premenopausal breast cancer. The health professional's follow-up study showed that men who drank two or more glasses were almost twice as likely to develop prostate cancer compared to those who didn't drink milk at all! Just to note, I'm talking about dairy in its purest state - milk straight from udder. This isn't even including the sugar and added hormones that are found in the grocery store milk most of us buy.

Vegetables And Fruit

One of my favourite films growing up was Spider-Man. I remember there was a scene in Spider-Man 2 where a group of robbers hijack a vehicle and almost run-down Peter Parker on his moped. Peter, using his spider sense, back flips off of his moped all the way over the car and lands in the superhero position. He looks around to find two kids eyes wide and mouth gawking at him to which one of them asks... "How'd you do that?!" to which Peter replies "Uhh, workout, plenty of rest. You know... eat your green vegetables". The kid still wide eyed then says "That's what my mom's always saying, I just never actually believed her!"

I remember watching that as a young teenager thinking "Wow, if only it was that simple to be superhuman." Well, Peter Parker wasn't completely wrong. How many of us can say we're eating enough green vegetables? According to NHS choices in the UK, it's recommended we eat 5 fruits and vegetables a day. Dr Alison Tedstone, the chief nutritionist at Public Health England, explains that the 5 a day number should be a baseline for a healthy balanced diet and the number should be closer to 10. Dr Joel Fuhrman however takes it a step further in his book *Super Immunity.* In it he states:

"Modern science has advanced to the point where we have evidence that the right raw materials and nutritional factors can double or triple the protective power of the immune system. If you learn to fill every cell receptor lock with the right nutrient key and meet the demands of each cell, the body's defences take on superhero qualities—and you will hardly ever get sick again."

My ears pricked up at superhero quality (thank you Peter Parker!). Dr Fuhrman goes on to recreate the food pyramid where 30-60% of our calories should come from vegetables. 50% raw and 50% cooked. Vegetables shouldn't be an addition to a poisonous diet, rather we need to strip away the poisons and make vegetables the foundation of our fuel if we wish to feel superhuman and become biochemically sober.

All vegetables were not born equally however. Vegetables, like ourselves, are living organisms that have defensive qualities to survive. Dr Stephen Gundry, a renowned cardiac surgeon and famous for being Tony Robbin's doctor, points our attention towards something within many foods called lectin. Lectin is part of a living foods arsenal to defend itself against predators. After all, a plant doesn't have the same fight/flight response as we do so by containing lectins it can give us nasty symptoms such as diarrhoea, vomiting and nausea. Lectins work by clinging onto cells in the lining of our intestines and nerve cells and break down communication within the immune system. They can even perforate the gut which is the primary cause for leaky gut syndrome. They cause toxic and inflammatory reactions. Sound familiar? That's right, gluten is a form of lectin.

Any vegetables containing seeds are technically a fruit so if we want to remove the majority of lectins within our veggies then make sure you remove the seeds, peel and wash.

Some veggies that are seen with real heroic processes are cruciferous vegetables. When cruciferous vegetables have their cell walls broken down via blending or chopping, it creates a chemical reaction that converts their sulfur-containing compounds into isothiocyanates. These are proven to have some great immune boosting effects as well as anti-cancer properties. In some population studies, just 3 servings of cruciferous vegetables per week decreased risk of prostate cancer by up to 41% compared to 28 servings of other vegetables a week which decreased risk by 33%. Something in these leafy greens, hey?

Below I have written a list that seems to be some of the best vegetables to line the foundation of your superhuman pyramid with. It doesn't mean others shouldn't be included, I just thought a nice list would be handy to get you started:

Asparagus, Bell Peppers, Bok Choy (Pak Choi), Broccoli, Brussels Sprouts, Cabbage, Carrot, Cauliflower, Celery, Collards, Fennel, Kale, Leeks, Lettuce, Olives, Parsley, Radishes, Spinach, Watercress.

When many people talk about fruits and vegetables they often make the mistake of clumping the two in the same category. I purposely called this section Vegetables and Fruit and not the other way around for that reason. Very often our "5 a day" can be confused for eating 5 fruits instead of 5 vegetables. I remember many years ago working at a call centre – a girl opposite me had just finished eating a beautiful green apple before announcing "right, I need to eat 4 more!". I was a bit shocked as I wasn't sure what she meant. "4 more apples?" I asked. "Yes" she replied, "So I can get to my 5 a day".

She wasn't joking. Although plant based, fruit is often kindly referred to as nature's candy. Really it should just be called candy. Our ancestors ate fruit when it was in season and that was it. The sugar in the fruit kept us wanting more and it would raise the weight and fat on our bodies to keep us warm for the winter. Our genes are not used to consuming large levels of fructose (fruit sugar) all year round. Robert Lustig MD, a paediatric endocrinologist at the University of California concludes in his book *Fat Chance* that even normal levels of fructose daily can inhibit our performance.

We should aim to minimise fruits and consider it a treat while we stock up on more vegetables.

Fat Burning Hero

Eating fat and being fat is not the same thing. In fact, it would be fair to say that the amount of fat we eat has very little to do with obesity rates and much more to do with our addiction to fast acting carbohydrates (grains, refined sugar). Despite carbohydrates being an abundant food source all around us, before the time of agriculture the amount of carbohydrates available were minimal. This means that our genome is set for fat, not sugar, to be our primary source of fuel. Earlier on in the chapter I said we have approximately 5,000 calories available to us in sugar but 140,000 calories available in fat. Our brain does something very interesting when it's using one source of fuel over another.

As our brain is responsible for using 20 percent of the energy we give it, if we're feeling tired it is our brain that's slowing down, not our body. If we are running on sugar and burning through the 5,000 calories store, when we hypothetically burn 500-1,000 calories the brain will pick up on this and realise that as it's running out of 10-20% of its immediate glucose store and will slow the body down to lower energy expenditure. However, if it's running on fat as its primary fuel and fat is being unlocked from the fat cells and being transferred into glucose, then the body can expend 1,000 calories and have only burned off 0.7% of the energy available. Often if a marathon runner has been carb loading they can often hit something referred to as 'the wall', a moment where they have depleted their sugar levels and effectively 'crashed'. However, if they 'run through the wall' they start pulling from their fat stores for energy and they enter what is commonly referred to as 'the second wind'.

Mark Allen, 1997's 'World's Fittest Man' and one of the greatest triathletes in history, made a breakthrough when he started burning fat instead of carbohydrates. This revolutionised his performance leading to six Ironman titles with a top 3 finish in every race! In the endurance world, carbohydrate loading before a big race has become a dogmatic religion made famous by Dr Tim Noakes who was also known as 'High Priest of Carb Loading'. He dedicated the majority of his life to advocating the high carbohydrate approach to athletic performance. After years of spreading the word, he continued on with his research to then advocate fat as the primary fuel as opposed to carbohydrates. Can you believe the bravery of this man? Years of dedicating your career to one thought only to change your mind based on the evidence present. This is the example of a truly open-minded person. Carbohydrates went from a nutrient that would make you stronger and faster to a poison that over time would make you fatter, weaker and more prone to diseases such as heart attacks, dementia, strokes and diabetes.

Remember the Tarahumara tribe who could run for 100's of miles in one go? What fuel were they running on? You guessed it, a high fat diet. What about Stu Mittleman – the endurance runner who ran 1,000 miles in 11 days?! He was also running on fat – something he refers to as the slow burn. Rich Roll, the world record Ultraman athlete, has a high fat vegan diet and Lebron James, the famous basketball player, is well known for eating a paleo diet. The most common thing between all these people is that they are cutting out the poisons, eating a ton of vegetables and using fat for fuel and they are going the distance. They are fat burning heroes!

A study called PREDIMED, published in the *New England journal of health 2013,* took 7,500 Spanish adults with risk factors of heart disease and placed them on three different diets:

Mediterranean with lots of olive oil

Mediterranean with lots of nuts

A conventional low-fat diet

There were no calorie restrictions or weight loss goals set. The diets that were high in fat showed dramatic reductions in risks of heart disease (approximately 30%)! The PREDIMED study actually had to be terminated early as the group on the low-fat diet were showing no reductions in heart disease risk, and it was considered unethical to keep them on it when the high fat diets were exceeding expectations so greatly!

When changing to a high fat diet we stop significantly raising our sugar levels so we will be less prone to drops and consistent hunger. Remember the fast-acting carbohydrate milkshake compared to the slow acting one? The body can run perfectly with very little carbohydrates but it cannot run with very little fat. By shifting our source of fuel from sugar to fat we reprogram our fat cells to release their stored energy. This shifts our metabolism into a weight loss mode and gives us a surge of energy while increasing our sense of fullness. That's right, you don't go hungry on a high fat diet and you get to conquer your cravings!

The moment we tuck into something like a fast food burger our nucleus accumbens lights up, our blood sugar levels dramatically spike and we've taken in an incredible number of calories. But how often after a burger are you still hungry? Most people at a fast food restaurant could quite happily grab another burger. Despite the pleasure sensors in our brain lighting up and taking in lots of energy we are still nutrient poor. Our bodies are still craving foods that are rich with the right vitamins and minerals, plus in a short while our blood sugar is going to crash. This feeling does not happen when we are eating lots of good fats and vegetables. We feel so much fuller for longer and as we've been eating all the right nutrients our body thanks us and it repays us with surges of consistent energy, clear thinking and happy thoughts. By eating this way we change our microbiome and begin to reduce any inflammation – a process which only takes 6-14 days. Imagine that, in just two weeks being able to reboot your body so you're moving back into its evolutionary parameters. This makes us biochemically sober!

Like vegetables, all fats were not born equal. We love naturally occurring fats in foods – yes please. However, in most processed and industrialised foods, there will be high levels of something called trans-fats. Trans fats are more commonly found in vegetable oils and mostly involve an artificial process that adds more hydrogens to make them more solid and stable. They're cheap, easy to use and have a long shelf life so food processing companies love to use them. These vegetable oils, also known as hydrogenated oils, increase the LDL (bad cholesterol) and decrease the HDL (good cholesterol), increasing our risk of cardiovascular and cerebrovascular diseases like heart attacks and strokes.

We also have two types of essential fatty acids called omega 3 and omega 6 which are unsaturated fats that help regulate blood pressure, inflammatory responses and are also used for the construction of cell membranes to help with proper nerve functioning. Omega 6 fatty acids help produce pro inflammatory responses which is great if we need to fight infections, and omega 3 fatty acids keep inflammation in-check and help with lowering our risk of heart disease and cancers. According to anthropological research, our hunter gatherer ancestors ate a ratio of 1:1 keeping us healthy and well balanced. However most of us have an uneven ratio of 16:1! That's 16 omega-6 fats for every 1 omega-3. You can see why a ratio this off balance can lead to high levels of inflammation and eventually to other cardiovascular, cerebrovascular and neurological diseases as well as cancer and diabetes!

Here's a list of trans fats to add to your poisons list and avoid wherever possible: vegetable oils such as safflower oil, corn oil, canola oil, sunflower oil, soybean oil, cotton seed and peanut oil.

Anything that you see that has been fried or battered in any of these - add it to the poisons list. It screams inflammation and heart disease. When doing your grocery shopping it may not mention trans fats or omega 6, so look out for partially/hydrogenated oils or shortening e.g. in mayonnaise.

Here is a list of fabulous fats we can add to the list rich in omega 3, naturally occurring in food aiding terrific brain health: Avocado, coconut and coconut oil, almonds, walnuts, macadamia, olives, olive oils, MCT oil as well as many vegetables previously mentioned.

Supplements

Supplements can be quite a controversial topic, however after researching and looking at the views of the best experts in the field, they seem like a great addition to our primal eating. It is not something our ancestors would have taken but there's a good reason for that. The best description I have seen for this as to why most of us should be taking supplements comes from Dr Mark Hyman in *The Ultra-Mind Solution*.

"If people eat wild, fresh, organic, local, non–genetically modified food grown in virgin mineral-rich and nutrient-rich soils that has not been transported across vast distances and stored for months before being eaten . . . and work and live outside, breathe only fresh unpolluted air, drink only pure, clean water, sleep nine hours a night, move their bodies every day, and are free from chronic stressors and exposure to environmental toxins, then it is possible that they might not need supplements. Because we live in a fast-paced society where we pick up food on the fly, skip meals, eat sugar-laden treats, buy processed foods, and eat foods that have been chemically treated, we could all use a little help from a multiple vitamin/mineral supplement."

There you have it. The important thing to take into account is that supplements at best should be seen as a great addition to an already nutrient dense diet, not a substitute. They are a great cherry to the cake but that's it.

Dave Asprey is a world-renowned health expert. In his book *The Bulletproof Diet*, after talking to many of the planet's best physicians, he gives his top 10 supplements to add to our primal eating:

Vitamin D, Magnesium, Vitamin K2, Vitamin C, Lodine, EPA/DHA (Krill Oil), Vitamin A, Selenium, Copper, Vitamin B12, and Folate.

So, how do we become Fat Burning Heroes? Most of it is dependent on the fuel we put into our body. Stocking up on our green vegetables, high fats like avocados and oils, nuts and seeds. Some meats and fish can be good and eliminating the poisons such as high glycaemic carbohydrates and grains such as bread, potatoes, honey, rice, pasta and fruit.

However, a lot of fat burning is dependent on how we use that energy as well. One of the best things we can do when moving our body is to build a strong aerobic base by staying in our fat burning zone. This involves moving at a pace where our heart rate never goes above our aerobic threshold.

To find your aerobic threshold simply take your age from 180. If you are 35 years old = 180 - 35 = 145 beats per minute. Training at this rate can seem slow at first however as Phil Maffetone says:

"You work your way up a few heartbeats at a time. You adapt. The more workouts you do in the fat-burning zone, the easier they get; the easier they get, the faster you can go."

Phil, the coach and trainer of triathlete legends such as Mark Allen and Mike Pigg, has used the fat burning zone time and time again and the results have been consistent. "They recover faster from workouts, blow past their old records in competition and leave chronic injuries behind. One reason they rarely get hurt is that they're no longer gritting through fatigue. When you go into oxygen debt, your form crumbles. Your head drops, your feet thump, your knees go cockeyed. You get sloppy and you pay for it."

Intermittent Fasting

There are benefits to fasting on a cellular, hormonal and anecdotal level. I'll go into these in more detail. Hunter gatherers have that name for a reason – most of their calories came from gathering and if a hunt was successful the rest could come from the prey. It is important to note that our ancestors were not eating the typical "3 square meals" a day. Our genes, our metabolism, the way we view food is all based on the fact we have no idea where our next meal is coming from, so let's gorge on what we can, when we can! This meant that they would also go for long periods of time, 16-72 hours with no food. Our bodies are evolved to handle this.

When we eat can be just as important as what we eat. When we are not burning fat, missing a meal can feel like death and we are expecting someone to walk in on us to find nothing but a pile of bones left on the floor. This doesn't mean we are necessarily hungry and we need food, it simply means our blood sugar levels are crashing. When we're intermittent fasting and burning fat, many of our hormones and our metabolism begins to stabilise and even within a few days we will notice a real dip in hunger. I am in no means talking about cutting calories. Our brain uses 20-30% of our calories and there is no way we can feel biochemically sober if our brain isn't getting the volume or quality of calories needed. By intermittent fasting I'm referring to a period where we stop eating at least 3 hours before we go to bed and do not eat for approximately the first 4 - 6 hours of waking. We are restricting our eating to an 8-hour window and then a 16 hour fast with only water.

This has some terrific proven benefits for our brain and body. The most common thing people will say when they're fasting in a fat burning zone is that they have a lot more focus and their cognitive function feels boosted.

This makes sense as our ancestors would have needed the most concentration to hunt food when they were hungry. Our cognitive function is never so sought after as when we need to fuel our bodies. The body has stopped expending energy having to metabolise food so instead the body has time to metabolise itself.

If you were stuck in a house with a snowy blizzard outside and only had a fire to keep you warm, once the wood had gone what would you throw in the fire first to keep it being fuelled? The answer would obviously be all the things you value the least.

To keep our bodies going and by giving our digestion system a break, our body begins a process called cell apoptosis which essentially is the death and recycling of cells. If there is a toxin that the body doesn't have time or energy to get rid of, it is stored away as fat. Cell apoptosis promotes the death of all those ill and dead cells that don't need to be there, it excretes and recycles them. If we fast for up to 3 days we actually kill off our white blood cells. Sounds terrible, doesn't it? But our body has a survival tool and actually ends up creating a whole new set of white blood cells rebooting our entire immune system.

As well as this, fasting helps with our cognitive function. In the MOVE chapter I said that exercise promoted BDNF (Brain Derivative Neurotropic factor), a protein promoting new signalling pathways. Fasting also does this, producing BDNF! It also increases synaptic plasticity which is the strengthening between the neurons I mentioned in the THINK chapter. Synaptic signalling is one element of that process that is fundamental to our learning and memory. By strengthening the gap between neurons the bond between those two nerve cells becomes closer and the signal can pass through more effectively.

Even hormonally there's been some great proven benefits. During the Dairy section I mentioned a hormone called IGF-1. High levels of IGF-1 are often linked to a multitude of cancers. Fasting has shown links with reducing the hormone IGF-1 and boosting hormones such as HGH (great for increased energy and exercise performance), testosterone (primary sex hormone in men) and LH (controls the production of sex hormones by the ovaries).

We should be drinking lots of water daily (half your body weight measured in lbs, drink that in ounces. E.g. 180lbs = 90oz of water per day). Personally it's the only thing I drink. We need to be drinking even more water when we're fasting. If our body is cleaning out all the dead cells we need to make sure we are giving it more than enough liquid to be able to wash these out of our body. Something else we need to consider is keeping on top of our mineral intake. Salt, magnesium and potassium are all critical if we want the cell signalling in our body to stay on peak – we especially need sodium for that. By adding just ½ - 1 teaspoon of salt into our water in the morning our body assimilates salt more effectively when we wake up and we'll have more energy. Lots of water and added sodium allows our cell membranes to be more permeable. Imagine a bit of salt water as the key to open the door to your cells making it easier for nutrients to move in but also to get the waste out!

In this chapter I haven't spoken much about weight loss or muscle growth but as I mentioned at the beginning, this isn't a book about fitness. It's about building the foundations for a healthy and happier life. To become biochemically sober and allow your brain and body to work in accordance with the genetic set up it has evolved for. The reason I called this chapter FUEL is because when we look at it in its simplest form, that's what food is. Yes it can bring people together and set off our pleasure centres, but it's primarily what our body needs to survive and thrive! Fuel is another principle that allows us to move further and faster to our destination to being a better CEO, a better athlete, a better partner, a better parent. I hope you have gained a great insight into some new strategies so you can unleash a more energetic, smarter, stronger and more consistent you.

We don't need to put ourselves under stress throughout this programme. This is never about eliminating poisons for the rest of our lives. We are changing what we repeatedly do, most of the time. No one got fat from eating one pizza! The greatest rule I know is the 80/20 rule – simply stick to this at least 80% of the time!

Fuel is an extremely controversial topic so the best thing you can do is to try these basics and see if it works for you. When it comes to dramatically changing your diet you should always consult a health professional first, especially if you are pregnant, taking medication (particularly for diabetes), or require medical supervision. By ignoring this warning there could be a risk to your health and in particular a risk of hypoglycaemia.

FUEL Chapter Summary

- The average diet results in a 2lbs increase in body fat. If we wish to change our eating patterns to give sustainable results we must change it to something we believe we can do forever.

- There is no perfect diet for everyone, just key fundamentals. The best way to determine the most optimal diet for you is to take the tests listed within the Diets Don't Work section.

- The gut is referred to as 'The Second Brain' as it can work independently of the brain and possesses a similar number of neurotransmitters. It manufactures 80-90% of the serotonin in our bodies and is responsible for 70% of our overall immune system.

- Eating toxic foods inflames the gut. This sends stress signals across our immune and nervous systems and through the vagus nerve, where it eventually gets picked up by our brain.

- All degenerative conditions are inflammation. Inflammation can lead to brain disorders such as dementia, Alzheimer's and strokes.

- Having gut inflammation inhibits the manufacturing of serotonin and can lead to depression.

- Our gut microbiome (the community of micro-organisms that line the gut) have the ability when changed to alter our neurobiology and reduce or increase our neurological response to stress.

- When it comes to our health in modern society it's more important that we focus on what we don't eat than what we do eat.

- Fast acting carbohydrates like sugar light up a part of the brain called the nucleus accumbens which is our pleasure centre, making it addictive. It has very little to do with the taste and nutrient value of a food/drink that makes it so appealing.
- Carbohydrates can be measured on a Glycaemic Index (GI) which gives an indication of how fast sugar is absorbed into our bodies. The higher the GI the steeper the blood sugar spike and the heavier the crash.
- Our hunger has very little to do with how much we're eating but more with how our blood sugar levels fluctuate. The more fast acting carbohydrates we eat the hungrier we will be.
- All calories are not equal in our body and even on a calorie deficit if the majority of our diet is carbohydrates it is still possible to gain weight.
- Sugar can suppress the immune system and cause inflammation. It feeds cancer cells and has been linked to breast, ovarian, prostate and rectal cancer. Sugar can weaken eyesight and cause premature aging (skin & general) and increase the risk of Alzheimer's disease. On top of this, sugar can cause auto immune disease, arthritis, asthma, heart disease, migraines and multiple sclerosis.

- Grains, including whole wheat, are amongst the highest GI foods. Genetically, chemically or structurally modified grains of today's age were not available to us for 95% of the time we've had these genes. For many of us our genes have not adapted in how to process these foods properly, and in most cases grains can cause inflammation leading to brain fog and other degenerative conditions.

- Fast digesting carbohydrates reduce verbal memory performance, working memory, selective attention and executive function. Grains are the new alcohol, taking us away from biochemical sobriety.
- Through the consumption of animal proteins in dairy they can leach calcium from our bones, giving us a calcium deficit.
- Countries with the highest consumption of dairy are also the countries with highest levels of osteoporosis.
- Dairy didn't enter our diet as homo sapiens until 7,500 years ago when we began to rear animals.
- The majority of the population is lactose intolerant. The gene which produces the enzyme lactase (a protein that is needed to digest lactose in milk) is switched off after infancy. However, in some people it can be expressed for the rest of their lives.
- We are the only species that habitually drinks another animals milk. We're also the only species to continue to continue drinking milk after infancy.
- Cows milk is a medium that transports the hormones and chemical components to turn a baby calf into a full-grown cow. It doesn't matter what we do to it, that's its prime purpose. It leads to increased levels of estrogen and decreased levels of testosterone. It increases the hormone IGF-1 which is linked to multiple types of cancer.
- The foundation of our food pyramid (30-60% of our calories) should come from vegetables: 50% raw and 50% cooked.
- Cruciferous vegetables have incredible immune boosting effects as well as anti-cancer properties.

- Plants do not have fight/flight responses like we do, so they contain toxins within them called lectins. These deter predators from eating them. Lectins cling on to the linings of our intestine and nerve cells, breaking down communication within the immune system. They cause toxic and inflammatory reactions, so avoiding plants/vegetables high in lectins can help increase health.
- Fruit should be seen as a treat due to them only being a tiny part of our ancestor's diet because they could only be eaten in season. The high sugar in fruit could helped them gain weight for the winter. Some research has shown that even normal levels of fructose (fruit sugar) daily can inhibit our performance.
- We have 5,000 calories available to us as glucose and 140,000 calories available to us as fat. To have more consistent energy, reduce inflammation, reduce hunger, reduce risk of cardiac conditions and increase our endurance we should switch our primary source of fuel from sugar to fat. This is done through a high fat low carbohydrate diet.
- The high levels of fat we consume should come from nutrient dense organic foods which are high in omega 3 fatty acids. This reduces inflammation and includes avocados, coconut oil and olives.
- Trans fats (hydrogenated oils) such as vegetable oil increase the bad cholesterol in our body and decreases the good cholesterol, and increases the risk of cardiovascular and cerebrovascular diseases like heart attacks and strokes.

- Eating lots of food high in omega 6 fatty acids disturbs our omega 3 to omega 6 ratio and can lead to high levels of inflammation.
- Intermittent fasting (eating within a 6-12 hour window, fasting for a 12-18 hour window) gives our digestive system a break and promotes the removal of ill and dead cells we don't need. It also promotes BDNF (cognitive function), reduces IGF-1, and boosts HGH, LH and testosterone.
- We should drink lots of water when fasting so that our body can successfully excrete all the dead cells.

COLD

"To me God is cold. Cold is a noble force, it is merciless but righteous. It is my teacher bringing me back to the inner nature, the way it was meant to be"

Wim Hof

A Warm And Comfy Caveman

We have become warm and comfy cavemen with awful thermostats! What I mean by this is that part of our evolutionary legacy that we have completely forgotten about is our ability to withstand huge temperature fluctuations. Remember the phrase 'if you don't use it, you lose it'? The same thing applies to the way we handle the temperature around us. If we go back to the times of our ancestors, they didn't have central heating. Even if we look back 50 years ago we didn't have central heating. Cavemen didn't have thermal vests. They were either naked, wore minimal clothing or animal skins. Just like our physiology these days, by sitting down for 12-14 hours a day, our body spends almost every day in a constant warm temperature box. We wake up and thankfully our radiators have already come on, so we're waking up to a lovely warm bedroom that's just comfy and cosy to our taste. We go and have a lovely warm shower to relax us even further, contained in a vessel filled with steam. We get out and use a warm fluffy towel, put a warm bath robe on us so we don't get a chill, put on tumble dried and ironed clothes. We then have a hot coffee or tea, a nice warm drink to give us the kick we need. Get in our car and pop the heater or seat warmers on. Get in the office, either air conditioned or central heating blazing, and probably have another hot drink. You can see where this is going can't you?...

Over the last few decades we've been able to change our environment around us so we are in constant comfort. You'd think our body would be thriving... less energy to expend and less worry about survival, but our body is suffering for this. Remember, comfort kills.

Our veins and arteries won't have had much practice in this case being able to constrict and dilate. Vasoconstriction and vasodilation are vital when it comes to being able to heal and transport oxygen effectively around the body. If our blood vessels aren't working as effectively they can cause things like strokes, heart issues and reduced healing abilities. What this also means is that the brown fat in our body starts to become reduced as it's no longer needed. We have 2 different types of fat on our body. Brown adipose tissue (brown fat) and white adipose tissue (white fat). The white fat in our body is the fat we recognise most, especially in western society because that's the fat where we store our unused calories. If we see someone who is obese it is because they have too much white fat on their body, not brown fat. Brown fat's primary purpose is to burn calories in order to produce more heat. Babies are born with a lot of brown fat because they don't have the muscles to shiver if they are cold, the brown fat keeps them warm. In fact, if it's fully activated, brown fat can generate heat up to 300% more than any other tissue in the body. It has been said that just 2oz of brown fat in the body appears to be capable of burning several hundred calories per day. If we want to be able to burn calories more effectively and use fat as a great energy source, having more brown fat and less white fat is a great start. There's even been studies to suggest that age related declining bone health is due to a loss of brown fat. If we continue to have higher levels of brown fat on our bodies then we may have stronger bones. As well as the weight lifting I mentioned to help increase our bone density - brown fat can be another tool to make that happen. What's a great way to build our levels of brown adipose tissue? Cold exposure!

By manipulating the temperature around us throughout the day and being a warm and comfy caveman we are missing out on a huge list of benefits to our physical and mental health. Something as simple as a cold hit could rectify this. The cold is nothing to be fearful of. Remember this is part of our evolutionary legacy that we simply haven't tapped into for a while.

If you feel like giving your ego a kick, simply visit Youtube and watch how many children in Siberia start their day at school. They go outside in their underwear through the snow, pick up a bucket of cold water and throw it over their heads! They do this, believe it or not, for health reasons. You may be so overwhelmed by the benefits of cold exposure that instead of saying to people "Put your jacket on, you'll catch a cold" you'll be saying "Don't take a jacket, you don't want to catch a cold".

Wim Hof The Iceman

Over the last few years, Wim Hof also known as 'The Iceman', has gone from a Dutch daredevil to an international celebrity. He has set over 20 Guinness World Records and has baffled scientists across the planet. He's appeared in numerous documentaries for the BBC, Vice and others including 'Stan Lee's Superhumans'. He has appeared on the show 'Daredevils', done TED talks and much more. He's become famous for his superhuman like cold endurance abilities.

If someone is subjected to extreme cold water for over 20 minutes their internal body temperature starts to drop. Even by dropping by 2 degrees centigrade, the average person starts to suffer from hypothermia. By being in the cold water for an hour you'll most likely die.

Wim was once able to stand within a block of ice for 1 hour and 52 minutes without suffering hypothermia. Some would say that wasn't even his most extraordinary feat. He's run a marathon above the arctic circle and climbed Everest only wearing shorts. He hasn't only record set records in cold endurance, he's hung off one finger at an altitude of 2,000 meters and has run a full marathon in the Namib desert without water consumption. You can see why people refer to him as superhuman.

Being a superhero-nut and a self-confessed geek myself, learning there are real life superheroes out there was a pretty exciting concept, so I knew I had to meet him! In December 2016 I flew out to Poland and spent a week in the mountains with Wim and his team, learning how to endure the cold. At the time it amazed me how quickly my body adapted but like we understand now, I was simply tapping into my evolutionary legacy left behind by my ancestors. Through Yogic Breathing and regular cold dips in icy water, my body soon learned to adapt to the cold and I too felt I was superhuman. One evening I was able to eat dinner with him and we chatted for 2 hours. Without a doubt he is an incredible human being. On the 5th day of training I ended up climbing Mount Sněžka, the highest point in Czech Republic and much higher than any mountain in the UK. I did this in minus 6 degrees Celsius, wearing only shorts and shoes. What amazed me though is how easy it felt. Since then I have had the privilege of climbing the UK's highest mountains in minus 5 to minus 15 degrees Celsius in only shorts and shoes. I'm hoping to set a world record of my own soon!

Despite these feats seeming superhuman, Wim insists that whatever he's capable of everyone can learn. The truth of the matter is that for thousands of years people have been doing what Wim can now do. Tibetan Monks have been famous for participating in a practice called Tummo Meditation, which simply means 'Inner Fire'. This allows them to heat up their bodies just through their breathing and meditation. In fact, they've been known to hold contests that involve a blanket being dipped in icy water, wrapped around themselves, and just by using the heat of the body they're able to dry these blankets off. Some have been known to get through 20 blankets in one night!

What Wim is more famous for is bringing Tummo Meditation into the scientific spotlight. Scientists have been able to test his internal body temperature when he's enduring the cold and they can see in the time he's spent in the ice, his internal body temperature never drops.

The most fascinating study that Wim's been part of that has really baffled scientists is his ability to consciously alter the effectiveness of his immune system. In a study done at Radboud University Medical Centre in 2014 a group of 12 people were trained in Wim Hof's Method to undergo an experiment. They were given an E.coli vaccine to induce inflammation and this would normally lead to flu like symptoms.

A control group of 12 participants were also given this vaccine but did not receive any of Wim's training. All 12 participants who'd had the Wim Hof training showed far fewer flu like symptoms, lower levels of inflammation and increased plasma epinephrine levels. In short, the people who had the training were able to consciously activate their sympathetic nervous system and increase their immune system, compared to the control group who couldn't. This is something that before 2014 scientists thought impossible.

Wim has taken "mind over matter" to the next level, to not just control emotions consciously but also control subconscious processes consciously.

Why Become An Iceman

Why Become An Iceman? Let's run through some of the benefits of cold exposure. Why do we want to shake our body out of the level of homeostasis we've become so accustomed to? Within the FUEL principle I brought up the idea of inflammation and how this is often linked to depression. But not just depression, anytime where our health has been affected negatively – inflammation is involved! Let's talk about a cytokine (a small protein that is evolved in cell signalling) called TNF-Alpha. This cytokine is an inflammatory cytokine, meaning it promotes the signalling of inflammation in our body. We see it involved in almost every disease, from diabetes type 2 to cancer. In an ideal world, to stop this inflammation or at least reduce it, we'd want to inhibit that inflammatory cytokine – that's where our warm friend the cold comes in!

When we're exposed to the cold we release a neurotransmitter called noradrenaline, also known as norepinephrine. The primary function in this is to enable the brain and body to be ready for action. It increases arousal and alertness, promotes vigilance and focuses attention. Just by those descriptions you can tell we would usually use this in the flight/fight response but as we're releasing noradrenaline in the cold **consciously**, we are firing this hormone without any of the other stress hormones being released that make us feel panicked. We are getting all the sharpness of the flight/fight response without any of the fear – what a gift! Noradrenaline/norepinephrine inhibits TNF-Alpha and that reduces inflammation. By reducing inflammation it means the cold may also help heal injuries and speed up our recovery.

We can see that the cold is actually another tool we can use to allow our body to flourish because we have less inflammation. Actually, it can also reduce depression as well because as previously mentioned, very often depression can be an extreme case of inflammation. If you have ever watched the documentary *The doctor who gave up drugs* one of the case studies used was a 24-year-old women named Sarah. She'd been on anti-depressants since the age of 16. Then, simply by cold swimming twice a week for 3 weeks she was able for the first time in 8 years to half her medication.

Let's just think of another benefit noradrenaline/norepinephrine gives us. If you have a cold shower in the morning (and it doesn't necessarily need to be cold first thing – you can end your warm showers with a cold blast for 30 seconds – 1 minute), by releasing that neurotransmitter in your body you'll suddenly be more alert, focused and attentive for the rest of the day. How many of us are walking into work in the mornings feeling sluggish and not fully awake yet? When we have noradrenaline running through our brain and body we have no choice other than to be on peak. I know I'd certainly prefer to start my day feeling alert and ready rather than feeling like I need a rest before I've even begun!

Studies have shown that when people take cold showers over warm showers it causes their white blood cell count to increase. Cold water immersion also has links with increases of T and B lymphocytes which are the cells used to defeat pathogens, meaning it increases and strengthens our immune system.

Everything to some extent is stress, even breathing in your body right now is causing a type of stress. But just like exercise, there is good stress on the body and bad stress on the body. The good stress is usually referred to as eustress (euphoric stress). The cold on the body in certain contexts is also referred to as eustress. The reason I say certain contexts is because by willingly getting into an ice bath or cold shower can be a very different biochemical process to unexpectedly falling through a sheet of ice on a lake.

If you have access to my 7 Steps online course I share a video on how to take a cold plunge and you'll be able to witness first-hand how my biochemistry changes.

Mitochondria Part 2

I want to take you back briefly to the quadrillion powerplants existing in our bodies – the mitochondria that help take in nutrients and give our cells energy. What would be just effective as having a fully functioning and effective powerplant? Having more of them! Imagine if we could not only improve the efficiency of our mitochondria but also increase the number. That alone would give us more energy and increase our athletic performance. We'd be able to tap into this abundant power throughout the day without stopping. Well, guess what we can use to increase our mitochondria?! You guessed it... the cold!

The cold can be responsible for a lovely scientific process called mitochondrial biogenesis, which simply means making more mitochondria. Exercise also does this by the way – just saying. The cold switches certain genes on to do this, exercise switches on others. If you want the greatest benefit then do both! By having more mitochondria we increase our aerobic capacity. My best friend recently did the Camino (a long walk through Spain) and very often on this journey he was walking up to a marathon a day. He was in average shape when he started doing this but his endurance was remarkable compared to many of his friends. As he didn't do any training for this he put his endurance down to the fact he has more mitochondria in his body! A short cut to more mitochondria can be seen as your own athletic performance drug... use the cold!

Sauna

At this point you may be saying "Les, you had me at hello: Thinking differently... got it! Breathing fully... yep I can do that. Move my body? Makes sense. Eating clean... perfect. But, cold?! There's no way I can do a cold shower. And an ice lake? Forget it!" Well, to you my friend, I say do not fear as I have another solution.

At the beginning of this chapter I wrote that we need to get away from being the comfy caveman when it comes to temperatures. I've explored the extreme cold but we can also get near enough identical benefits by exploring the extreme heat. So, for the haters out there who don't think the cold can be your warm friend, I introduce to you the power of sauna.

Just by subjecting your body to hyperthermic conditions, your body quickly adapts and reduces the negative effects associated with elevations in core body temperature. This means that the next time you're exposing yourself to heat such as during a race or a workout, your body will be able to optimise its systems.

There's a great video online from one of world's top heat exposure experts Dr Rhonda Patrick PH.D where she goes into the physiological depths about what's happening when we're exposed to hyperthermic conditions like a sauna, and more importantly the benefits they can provide for us. Search 'Rhonda Patrick' on YouTube and you'll be blown away by the value from her.

Very often when it comes to taking saunas, people are desperate to know the ideal temperature, session time and frequency required to reap those benefits. There's some brilliant studies from Finland which can give us an idea on some of those numbers! For the minimal benefits of reducing cardiovascular disease, mortality and Alzheimer's risk, sitting in a sauna for about 20 minutes at 79 degrees Celsius for 2-3 times a week would be perfect. The study showed a 20% lower risk of cardiovascular disease and a 20% lower risk of Alzheimer's disease compared to men who only used the sauna once per week! However, compared to men who used the saunas 4-7 times a week, it found those men had a 50% lower risk of cardiovascular disease and a 65% lower risk of Alzheimer's compared to those who used it just once per week.

The best results for sauna sessions when it comes to aerobic capacity are of the sauna sessions done post workout. When I told you about my friend who walked across the Camino who believed his high endurance to be down to his increase of mitochondria, it wasn't down to regular cold exposure but through daily sauna sessions that he credits this achievement. The reason that this chapter primarily focuses on the cold as opposed to heat is because the time spent in the cold to get the benefits is a lot less, needing just 2-5 minutes per day compared to 20-30 minutes in a sauna – it's much more effective timewise. Also, you may not have access to a sauna. If you have a sauna at your local gym which you can use after you've moved your body then perfect. You now know all the reasons why! Don't have access to a sauna? Start the morning with a cold blast in the shower to get your blood moving and increase your tolerance slowly. You can still reap the health benefits.

COLD Chapter Summary

- Regular cold exposure improves our immunity and blood circulation.

- The cold can reduce inflammation, helping to reduce the risk depression.

- Cold exposure speeds up metabolism. This promotes weight loss.

- Cold plunges and/or cold showers increases alertness.

- Cold exposure reduces stress.

- Cold water speeds up muscle soreness and recovery.

- Cold exposure increases the mitochondria in our body giving us more energy.

- Heat exposure, like a sauna, also gives similar benefits to cold exposure over longer periods of time.

CONNECT

"Human beings need 3 basic things in order to be content: they need to feel competent at what they do; they need to feel authentic in their lives; and they need to feel connected to others. These values are considered 'intrinsic' to human happiness and far outweigh 'extrinsic' values such as beauty, money and status"

Sebastian Junger

Tribe

When we think about our lives now, we think of meeting with friends as a "nice" activity. It's lovely to have a chat with a mate, catch up with a bestie! It's a symbol of pride to be an 'independent adult' living our own lives and seeing friends occasionally, but that's not what our genes had in mind when we were born.

95% of the time that we have had these bodies we were living in the hunter gatherer lifestyle. We were always surrounded by our tribe. Instead of being well-to-do modern day humans our primitive wiring is much more similar to that of wolves. We were a pack – we'd sleep together, eat together, hunt together, gather together. Very often we would have non-monogamous relationships like bonobos and chimpanzees. We would have sex together too. Instead of sex being about domination and a function of ownership of one's partner, like bonobos it was a way to increase social activity and connect with the group. We would be parents to all the children, not just our own. In the book *Sex at Dawn*, when an anthropologist asked a member of an indigenous tribe about how sad it was that he couldn't look after his biological children specifically, the member of the tribe smiled and said "I don't get to love just one child, I get to love all of them". When we speak in terms of evolution it would be logical to think that we put our children first due to our DNA having a stronger link – of course we want to protect our DNA over genes that are less similar to our own (other children or strangers). However, you only have to speak to parents of adopted children to understand that they too would be willing to die for children that aren't part of their inherited genes. It's difficult to determine which child is your own if everyone is having sex with everyone. The sense of ownership of 'my partner' 'my house' 'my land' 'my child' was more likely a concept that would start to have formed when the agricultural revolution came and we became part of larger settled communities. Living in smaller hunter gatherer tribes commanded a forced sense of egalitarianism. If you were to hoard more food for yourself than for the rest of the tribe this would be seen as a taboo action and highly frowned upon. When it's a matter of survival, a strict sense of fairness must be applied in a hunter gatherer society. If I were to put myself and my needs before any members of my tribe I would likely be kicked out or severely punished. The moment I'm on my own outside society and fending for myself in the jungle, my probabilities for surviving begin to plummet. This causes us to move into the limbic system and operate within the parameters of depression, anxiety and anger. By using those opt out clauses we enter the states as to which we're most likely to survive in.

Something to repeat here is that the emotional mind doesn't just punish us if we are doing something that threatens our survival. It also rewards us when we're doing something that increases our chances of survival – so we're encouraged to do it again. Being in the company of others is a perfect example of this. The moment we are physically in the presence of another human we start to release the chemical oxytocin throughout our bodies, something often referred to as the feeling of receiving a warm hug. When a mother gives birth to a new born baby she has huge levels of oxytocin in her body which creates a strong bond to that child, therefore she's more likely to care for it. Oxytocin also promotes breastfeeding as well as causing higher levels of trust in groups of men. By producing this biochemical feedback loop we feel mentally better every time we are taking an action that involves self-sacrifice and the promotion of group welfare.

It's a peculiar thought, isn't it? That the only reason you're able to read this now is because at some point someone was willing to dedicate and sacrifice their time for your survival. It was only through their love (even if it didn't always feel like it) that allowed you to be sitting where you are today. Humans, unlike certain animals, are helpless at birth. We depend on others to survive and others depend on us to survive – it's a wonderful circle of giving value.

We are wired to connect, not just in society but even on an individual level. Touch plays such an important role in our health. In the 1950s a primatologist and psychologist called Harry Harlow conducted an infamous experiment with baby rhesus monkeys who were separated from their mothers and presented with 2 new man-made surrogates. One 'mother' was made out of warm cloth, while the other was an uninviting metal frame put together with a mesh of wires. The metal mesh mother had with it an artificial nipple that dispensed milk when sucked on. As a survival mechanism it could be predicted that the baby would stay with the mother that fed it, the mother that provided it with nourishment and the right fuel. However, the study found that the baby monkeys would take the nourishment as quickly as possible before returning to the cloth covered mother. Being wrapped in cloth provided the baby with a warm softness that could give the illusion of affection and comfort. In fact, photos can be seen from this experiment where the baby is taking the milk from the artificial nipple on the metal mother whilst still clinging on the cloth covered mother. This shows clearly that touch, warmth and affection are vital to the health of baby primates, including humans.

Another example to re-enforce the importance of touch is that Northern European and North American societies are the only ones in history that make very young children sleep alone in such high numbers. In 2 American studies of middle class families during the 1980s 85% of children slept alone in their room, a figure that raised to 95% between families who were considered as "well educated". It's very common in these cultures that children instinctively bond and become attached to cuddly toys, stuffed animals and even blankets. This is a self-soothing mechanism for reassurance believed to be caused by isolation from parents, as this is practically unheard of in other cultures where young children sleep close to their parents. This isolation of young children is another evolutionary mismatch to our natural coding. When we look at primates we can see they almost never leave their babies unattended as this would increase the risk of being vulnerable to predators. This self-soothing need we have as humans is a survival instinct disguised as a reward system.

It can seem quite cold hearted, can't it? Almost pessimistic that our desire to give and contribute to others can be seen as no more than a 'gimmick' to better our chances of survival. Once I'd learnt that giving, contributing and in some sense loving could all be symptoms traced back to an evolutionary principle around my own survival, I felt like I'd lost a part of me. And it *is* sad if you look at it that way, but then it hit me – actually, isn't it wonderful that it feels so good when we do something for others? Just because we know the reason why that is, it doesn't mean the feeling we get from that action is any less valuable, any less magical. Remember the Primal Life motto: *enjoy everything* – knowing the evolutionary reason behind the gift of giving isn't an excuse to stop loving, it shouldn't make that feeling any less meaningful. Isn't it wonderful that out of the five billion species that have existed on Earth, we happen to be the one of the few that can feel that desire for connection. Over the millions of years it has taken us to evolve we have embedded in us, in the very fibre of our being, a biochemical process that allows us to experience joy and a sense of belonging when we connect, contribute and support our fellow humans. Studies have shown if we were to give money to a stranger in need, we would feel a greater sense of reward from that process (by giving away something and contributing) than the stranger would feel from receiving it. You know in the past when you've truly given something it feels great, but this was second nature in hunter gatherer tribes.

218

Something to note is that tribes were a lot smaller in these caveman societies, averaging 50-60 members. A phenomenon known as Dunbar's Number shows that we find it near enough impossible to hold a meaningful relationship with more than 150 people.

Community

In prehistory there was often much more danger around than what we experience in the 21st century, including high child death rates, violence from other tribes, scarcity of food and climate disasters. It was because of these dangers that we were forced to act together and most likely prosper if we acted as a community. What this means for us now is that not only do we thrive when we are together, but we actually thrive better in times of adversity. The moment there is danger around and we're banded together our bodies are more likely to release higher levels of neurotransmitters because that is what's needed to give us the strength to get through the adversity. In horrific circumstances where places have been affected by war or natural/man-made disasters, we have found that during and after the event these communities begin to flourish. In these moments we see modern-day society become much more similar to our hunter gatherer ancestors, adopting a more egalitarian approach. New Orleans for example experienced a drop-in crime rate after the Hurricane Katrina. When we look back to the Blitz in World War 2, the city of London experienced 57 consecutive days of German bombers dropping thousands of tonnes of high explosives, killing hundreds of people at a time. Mini communities started forming in bomb shelters and tube stations, with conduct so good that the police never had to be called out to maintain crowd control. The communities took it upon themselves to uphold this primitive sense of fairness. One man had written in a massive concrete structure known as the Tilbury Shelter that 'Ten thousand people had come together without ties of friendship or economics, with no plans as to what they were meant to do'. It was a time where you'd think mass hysteria would be at its highest. Many would have assumed that communities would be failing to stick together. Horrors such as World War 2, where hundreds of bodies were being pulled out of rubble daily, you'd think stress disorders and individual psychosis would be extremely high. After all, surely mental illness and imminent danger are correlated? It seems however that the opposite is true. Psychiatrists watched in puzzlement as they witnessed their patient's symptoms reduce during the raids. In fact, psychiatric hospitals throughout the country experienced their admissions decrease. This isn't an uncommon phenomenon. After the World Trade Centre fell in 2001, rates of suicide and crime all dramatically dropped. In a 1979 journal of psychosomatic research, Lyons noted "When people are actively engaged in a cause, their lives have more purpose, resulting with the improvement in mental health". And that's another important quality of connection, when we're part of a community it gives our lives purpose.

Connecting with people around us not only fulfils our need for attention and significance. When we're actively engaged in a community it gives our life meaning. Giving value and having a purpose in our tribe is another evolutionary quality encoded in our genes. If I wasn't the best mammoth hunter in my tribe then maybe I couldn't give enough value, and if I couldn't give enough value then maybe my tribe don't need me? If I'm not able to earn my place in my tribe by giving value unique to me, my chances of earning respect reduces and someone will be very unlikely to reproduce with me. We are the descendants of the cavemen who found a way to express value to their tribe. Another way of phrasing this is 'we are the descendants of those who found their purpose'. Let's say that I am a caveman who wasn't the best mammoth hunter... by possessing the genetic algorithm to find a purpose this could allow me to add value another way, by being the best cook, most efficient leader, or perhaps the best mediator to bring the community together. There's a million different ways that we could have served our community but it was that seed of purpose-driven behaviour that allowed the genes of that caveman and cavewoman to be passed on.

That still lives within us now; so many of us still possess the hardwiring that we have a purpose and if we haven't found a way to express that, what happens? It can cause an evolutionary mismatch that reduces the capacity of our biochemistry. We can see why mental health cases dropped in times of adversity; these patients were given a purpose to serve their community.

Everyone with a conscious brain for thousands of years has asked the big question 'what is the meaning of life?'. The best answer I have ever come across was from the Quantum Physicist Michio Kaku who expressed his belief that "Life doesn't have a meaning whatsoever. It is us that has the choice to put a meaning to it." We already know that meaning and purpose is a subjective quality. Michio goes into this further "If the world's smartest scientists got together and managed to find the meaning of life and put it into a magnificent equation on a blackboard, who would actually use it? No-one would react to that. Meaning is something we have to find for ourselves, it's our decision".

Another key component for us to become biochemically sober is to be part of a tribe/friendship group. To find a community that gives us a sense of belonging, a sense of meaning, and allows us to contribute in our own unique way. Simply by being in the presence of others we're able to release more oxytocin which gives us that increased sense of wellbeing and adds to mentally healthy behaviour.

The Illusion Of Connection

In the famous *Great Dictator Speech* by Charlie Chaplin, when referring to technology and communication he states "The very nature of these inventions cries out for the goodness in men - cries out for universal brotherhood - for the unity of us all." It's true… technology has connected the world. Within seconds we have the ability to communicate with another person in the most remote parts of the world, whether that's via telephone, email, social media or video call. We are in what the philosopher Ken Wilber refers to as 'the integrated age'. Simply within a few miles of where you live you will likely have access to different cuisines, different languages, different fashions and different cultures from all over the world. We are living in a time of the least amount of violence in human history and we've become more tolerant of other people's beliefs, backgrounds, skin pigmentation and lifestyle than ever before, due to our incredible ability to access information. It is without a doubt that technology has allowed us to widen our scope when it comes to the numerous lifestyles that are available for us to lead as humans. I remember once hearing from a fellow writer that "We have the most phenomenal invention of the world in our pockets. I can ask any question in human history, any fact a human has ever known, and it can give me an answer in seconds, yet most of us use this machinery to watch videos of cats".

In Psychology there is something known as a Pleasure Triangle. This simply means that if a particular action hits 3 specific criteria perfectly we will be more likely to take that action than any other choice. The 3 points that have to be hit are: avoid pain, receive pleasure and conserve energy as efficiently as possible. Technology allows us to do this perfectly. By using a laptop or phone I can order food to my home, communicate with my friends, purchase complex items and for many of us even conduct our work. I avoid pain by minimising my risk of dangerous incidents (safer indoors than outdoors), I gain pleasure by completing the tasks I need to do and I conserve energy by not even needing to leave the house. With social media, entertainment on tap and search engines, this technological utopia can allow us to function in society without even getting out of bed. A paradise at first but you can see the point that's trying to be made here... we have another evolutionary mismatch where it's become easier and easier to survive in isolation. In modern society we can now create a comfort zone in which it is the norm to experience long periods of isolation. Despite being able to function in communities like cities our tribe has increased from 150 to over 1,000,000 members and the sense of community is being lost. Our comfort zone has changed. Suddenly the community we had in the Blitz has transformed over the decades from having a comfort zone the size of a town, to being no bigger than a house and for many of us now our comfort zone (the place we feel most safe) is no bigger than our bedroom. It's never been so easy to draw the parallels between modern day depression and the hibernating caveman who pulled the rug over his head because the ice was too dangerous outside of his cave.

What's worse to a prisoner than sharing a room with a murderer or rapist? It's solitary confinement. There seems to be no higher level of retribution than forcing someone to be alone, but we don't always feel alone, do we? After all, our friends are only a click and a swipe away and suddenly we are one conscious being speaking to another. So, we are connected surely? Just like the baby rhesus monkey physically holding onto the cloth mother whilst reaching for milk from the metal mother, we too need physical interaction to release that flow of oxytocin in our body. Even though we have access to hundreds of friends on social media with the ability to contact them within seconds, we are hitting the 3 points of the Pleasure Triangle but despite conserving energy, this illusion of connection doesn't change our biochemistry. We are not receiving the warm hug of oxytocin that is so heavily embedded in our core needs as humans.

You can see that as the radius of our bubble of comfort has decreased over time, it has detached us further from our human need for connection, not only disturbing the release of oxytocin but also removing many of us from our sense of purpose.

Social media and communication through technology has not only given us an illusion of connection, it's also given us an illusion of competition. Technology has widened our scope to a larger community and has opened up our potential network to more than 3 billion people online. It has also raised our expectations. In a society 50,000 years ago, living in a tribe of 100-150, if we were to remove the extreme ages we'd have a finite selection of potential partners, so chances are you'd think of yourself as a pretty attractive person! For a teenager today, social media allows us to compare the mundane moments of our own lives to the photoshopped highlight reels of people around the world. It's much easier to feel inadequate in today's society than compared to our ancestors. Modelling agencies find the most gorgeous people on the planet and unveil them before our eyes consistently on billboards, televisions and through social media exposing us constantly to unrealistic standards of beauty.

Let's backtrack a second to the THINK chapter - "I am what I think about all day long" and "We are what we repeatedly do" - Everyday millions of companies are competing for our attention. Frequently they use scare tactics to make us buy their products, raise our expectations and barrage us with so called better ways to fit into our community. We are being given a subconscious message on repeat that we are not good enough and we do not belong... not yet anyway. To be approved by your community, buy this car! To be approved by your community and fit in, have a peachy perfect bum! To mean anything in this community and earn the approval of your peers, get this phone! Suddenly we've created something popularly referred to as FOMO, the fear of missing out. What is FOMO really, other than the fear of losing connection to the community? If you woke up one day and there was no one else on this planet and you were completely alone without competition or connection, would you have the same goals? Would you still want the fast car and the same house and job? Being the only person alive you could have all those things. You could have every car and move to a new mansion every day. But wouldn't something feel different?

It is not surprising that so many people in modern society are suffering from depression, anxiety, low self-esteem and body issues; when day to day we're being told on repeat that we're not good enough. Feeling alienated from our tribe is one of the greatest ways to kick our biochemistry out of balance. Remember the emotional mind can't tell the difference between fiction and reality. By being jacked-in to a virtual world where everyone seems healthy, happy and everyone is good enough but us, we are given unrealistic expectations and have built a false reality that has created a real symptom of low self-esteem. We are bombarded by these images and messages constantly that we forget the truth that 25% of people we meet are suffering from a mental health disorder and 35% are obese.

All of us have created an echo chamber of set values. Our moral principles, our diet, our fashion and our culture is being fed to us in a constant loop, forcing us to a fixed way of living, an unchanging reality that encourages the global belief that 'this is just the way life is'. Social media is a primary example of this. We 'friend' those who share our beliefs and delete those whose opinions we don't like, so we only get shown people who share our opinion in politics, religion and topical issues on the news. We soon forget that there is an entirely different reality available and on top of this the echo chamber is likely to contain issues that very often do not even directly affect us. However, as it's shown to us time and time again we are picking up knowledge that very often is useless, does not concern us and very often wastes our time.

It is for this reason that I don't watch the news. There.... I said it! Tribes in the Amazon had no knowledge about what was happening with the Maasai Tribe in Africa and they had no need to know. I'm not advocating that ignorance is bliss. I'm simply stating that taking on information that we can't apply to our own lives is useless. As Tim Ferriss says "Knowledge is useless. All the knowledge in the world and $4 will get you a coffee in Starbucks". The point here is that if we obtain knowledge that we can't put into application then we're just wasting time. Did you know that people who watch the news of a tragic event are likely to experience a trauma up to 6x more powerful than people who were actually there?! By someone showing us negative events constantly on repeat that are in no way connected to our lives we activate our emotional mind and we move into the parameter of depression anxiety and anger. By searching for news, research, events and topics on your terms in your own time as opposed to being flooded with irrelevant information, you're already halving the amount of stress going into your bucket each day. Trust me, if there's some national or international news that will directly affect you that's urgent for you, then you'll know about it!

Choose Your Tribe

A message universally shared with successful athletes, admired entrepreneurs and leaders of industry is that you are the average of the 5 closest people to you. Who you spend time with is who you become. Just like the way our genes have evolved to adapt to the environment around us, we adapt socially to fit in with the people around us. Our beliefs, our values, our financial earnings, our goals and our standards will usually correlate with that of those around us. Just take a moment and write down a list of the 5 people you spend the most time with. It might be friends, family, business partners or work colleagues. More often than not our reality will very often be synonymous to theirs.

When we want to move forward in our life we can usually experience a tremendous fear of failure. Very often it won't be the fear of failure for ourselves but the fear that our tribe will no longer love or respect us. "What will my parents say?" "What will my partner think?" "Will my friends mock or leave me?". In the 'Illusion Of Connection', I made the abundance of technology seem like an inherently negative concept. And yes… it does have its fair share of disadvantages, however once we are aware of what's happening we get to do something our ancestors never could - we get to choose our tribe! When I talked about the quickest hack to changing your state I said it was to change your breath. The quickest and most successful hack for raising your standards and increasing the level at which you participate in life is to change your tribe.

Our standards and the quality of our life increases as a by-product of the love and respect we crave from our tribe. If you're interested in space, horse-riding, spirituality, neuroscience, sewing, chess… it doesn't matter… we can use technology to set up situations to find like-minded people out there. I remember coming back from Poland having just learnt the Wim Hof Method. It was on this retreat that I met my best friend. To think I had to wait a quarter of a century to meet him, but now looking back on it - of course if I was to meet my best friend anywhere it would be there, a place that brings together people of similar passions and interests. At school, college or work we form a tribe out of necessity rather than choice. As peculiar as it seems, most of our friends in life are people who just floated into our timeline by chance. However, technology gives us the steering wheel to learn and spend time with who we want. Going to seminars and events are great places to form new tribes because you have a concentrated dose of people most likely holding similar belief systems as well as a similar standard for life. I came back to Plymouth where I was living at the time and realised it was time to change my tribe. I set up a free cold exposure group that anyone could attend. As you can imagine it attracted people who were all interested in health and wellbeing as well as personal development. I met like-minded coaches, doctors, alternative-therapists and surgeons. This allowed the learning curve for my passion to increase exponentially. Even though logically we know that statistically if there's 7 billion people on the planet there *has* to be at least a handful of people who like and feel the things we do, we just don't know that emotionally until we meet them.

Let's use technology to our advantage and build a tribe of our choosing. Join groups, online communities and go to real life events where the tribe of our choosing exists. I promise you that your life will change quicker than you knew possible.

One of the reasons I conduct events, seminars and retreats isn't just to provide strategies that will help people grow, it is to bring those like-minded people from all over the world together so they can form their own 'tribes' and potentially meet their potential new best friends and partners – it's an incredible sight to witness and an even better feeling to experience.

It can seem like a harsh message, however if we have friends that are holding us back and not empowering us to be the best versions of ourselves, then we need to cut them off. It sounds quite selfish, doesn't it? But there is a method to the madness. When you're on a plane and they give the safety announcement at the beginning about oxygen masks, what's the most important point they make? It doesn't matter whether you have someone next to you, a baby or someone with a disability, if those masks come down you always put it on yourself before helping others. Why? Because if you're not the clearest thinking version of yourself then there's no real value you can give to others. How much help can you be to other passengers if you cannot breathe properly? This exact philosophy stands in Buddhism. From the branch of Buddhism that I was taught it's believed that the sole purpose we have in this lifetime is to become enlightened and to stop our suffering. The motivation behind this quest for enlightenment isn't simply to stop our suffering, it's so we can show others the way to end theirs. The personal trainer Steve Maxwell gave a wonderful anecdote that said "All of us are walking around in a dark room and somewhere, unknown to most of us, there's a door we can open that will bring us into the light. Some of us want to get into the light so we can see again, others want to find that door so we can get everyone else out of the dark room".

If we want to give lots in life we need to have value to give, but that's not going to happen if we have stopped growing. This isn't about being selfish, it's about making the decision (remember, decision means to 'cut away from') to break away from a tribe that disempowers you and enter one that allows you to flourish and bathe in being the best version of yourself, so you can give more to your community.

If you look at any of the greatest achievers on the planet they never did it by themselves. All of them will have had a great support network (tribe) to help keep their standards raised and performance on peak. Arnold Schwarzenegger is a perfect example of a high achiever. To excel in four different careers when the odds were stacked against him is an incredible feat. This is a man who started off as an Austrian bodybuilder who became Mr Olympia 7 times in a row, became a millionaire through property investment, and after achieving the height of his bodybuilding career gave it up to become an actor. Of course, people laughed at him. First of all he had such an abnormal body compared to other Hollywood actors that he was unlikely to be able to fit into any normal roles. Alongside the way he looked, people mocked his accent. How on Earth could he be a top actor if people couldn't understand what he was saying?! On top of that he was mocked for his name. There is no way anyone can become an A-List superstar if people can't even pronounce his surname, surely?! However, he used this to his advantage. He never auditioned because he aimed for roles that no-one else would be able to fill due to not having his body. After filming, the makers of Terminator said that if they didn't find a Schwarzenegger they'd have to build one! "I'll be back" is one of the most famous lines in film history, all made famous by his accent that sounded robotic. He ended up becoming one of the highest grossing action stars of all time and his name is now synonymous with an action hero. After he'd done this he decided to run in politics and successfully became the Governor of a state whose name he can't even pronounce. Bill Burr openly jokes "Of course the guy thought he could get away with having an affair, he's been in 'the zone' for 20 years".

If you read the foreword of Tim Ferris' book *Tools of the Titans* it's written by Arnold and is titled 'I am not a self-made man'. Here's an extract of that foreword:

"Every time I give a speech, someone says it. As a self-made man, what's your blueprint for success?

But it is not true that I am self-made. Like everyone, to get to where I am, I stood on the shoulders of giants. My life was built on a foundation of parents, coaches, and teachers; of kind souls who lent couches or gym back rooms where I could sleep; of mentors who shared wisdom and advice; of idols who motivated me from the pages of magazines (and, as my life grew, from personal interaction).

I had a big vision, and I had fire in my belly. But I would never have gotten anywhere without my mother helping me with my homework (and smacking me when I wasn't ready to study), without my father telling me to "be useful," without teachers who explained how to sell, or without coaches who taught me the fundamentals of weight lifting.

If I had never seen a magazine with Reg Park on the cover and read about his transition from Mr. Universe to playing Hercules on the big screen, I might still be yodeling in the Austrian Alps. I knew I wanted to leave Austria, and I knew that America was exactly where I belonged, but Reg put fuel on the fire and gave me my blueprint."

So often we start on a journey of transformation and it somehow rings our ego bell that it'd be so much better if we could do this on our own. It just doesn't happen. We need our tribe if we want to thrive.

Whenever we're looking to develop ourselves to the next level, then like the caveman we need someone to be accountable to.

One of the biggest mistakes we make when we step on a new path to better ourselves is that we don't set up an accountability buddy, or if we do, we don't set ourselves with a good quality one. This doesn't necessarily mean they'll let you down, it may mean you just don't genuinely feel accountable to them and you won't feel awful if you let them down. A big part of this may be due to them having the same standards as the person you used to be, as opposed to the person you want to be. We see this all the time, don't we? I remember when I was consulting and I'd see people who had previously struggled with their weight who all agreed to go on a diet together and support each other but within a week they'd all have fallen off the bandwagon. This may not be down to the fault of the diet yet they all went in at the same level of attitudes when it came to their body. Unless one of the group had iron-clad will to support the rest, it would all crumble. Some people pay for an accountability buddy. What's a personal trainer? An accountability buddy! Yes, they provide you with strategies to lose weight, although if you wanted to you could find this information online for free. What we are really paying a personal trainer for is them to be someone who can hold us accountable for our actions and hold us without fail to the new standard for which we've set ourselves.

There is a lot of power in an echo chamber. If we want to take ourselves out of a negative downward spiral and put ourselves into an upwards growing one, we can choose our echo chamber! Sure, we might not have Richard Branson, Tony Robbins, Dalai Lama or Jessica Ennis-Hill in our closest circle, but we can still add them and others to our echo chamber through the books that we read, podcasts we listen to and the people we connect with on social media. By editing, filtering and choosing the data that surrounds us you can make the news, events and advice available to you on a daily basis be the ones that are going to benefit you most and allow you to flourish.

Shinrin Yoku

It makes sense to connect with other people but a connection that many of us still neglect is our connection to nature. We already know that moving our bodies reduces stress, however something that amplifies that stress reduction is where we move our bodies. Would it really surprise you to know that walking through nature offers huge anti-depressant effects? Close your eyes and imagine walking a couple of miles through a city surrounded by the noise of traffic, people talking and the smell of burning petrol...., or walk a couple of miles through a wood surrounded by the sounds of birds singing and gently trickling streams, where you are taken in by the scent of the undergrowth. After finishing that walk which one would we feel more tranquil in? It's not a coincidence when we listen to relaxing music that the track is often filled with sounds of nature. Nature relaxes us because it's our true genetic home.

Walking through nature has been heavily researched in Japan. In fact they have a specific process to make contact with the atmosphere of a forest and this is known as Shinrin Yoku, also known as forest bathing. Forest bathing is simply walking through a forest with purpose, walking mindfully and absorbing nature. It has shown to promote lower concentrations of cortisol and reduce blood pressure as well as pulse rate. By measuring cerebral activity (activity in the brain) we can see this also reduces technostress.

The Oxford English Dictionary describes technostress as stress caused by working with computer technology on a daily basis. However it is much more than this. In THINK I referred to the health and safety officer in your brain, constantly vigilant of everything going on around you, always scanning for potential threats. Within modern cities we're faced with yet another evolutionary mismatch as we cross a path never met by our ancestors - sensory overwhelm. Just walking through a city our minds become stimulated by a variety of loud noises, bright lights, large groups of strangers, traffic from all directions and much more. This can happen all within a 10 minute walk at lunch time. We have become desensitised to the overload, yet our health and safety officer has much more of a reason to be alert than ever before and this causes our stress buckets to fill.

When we are in nature we can say that the opposite is true. As opposed to walking through a sea of people in cities, only one or two are likely to cross our path in nature and we're more likely to greet them. Instead of cars speeding by at 40mph the only way we can come across something similar in nature is if it were a small pack of animals in the distance. The only time we are likely to encounter loud noises in nature is if disaster strikes or a large animal is nearby, in which case our survival could be threatened and it would be a situation where we would want our health and safety officer to raise its head. We always win we walk in nature!

Connecting to nature is simply another way to empty our buckets. The way forest bathing works isn't due to the lack of technostress but rather the biochemical reaction we have with the trees. Trees secrete a substance known as phytoncides which ward off harmful bugs and rot. However, by soaking in this compound it actually does our body some good.

At the risk of sounding like a free-love hippy, nature can remind us that we truly are connected to everything and everyone. Some of the world's most renowned academics in the science community find this to be an indisputable fact. When astrophysicist Neil deGrasse-Tyson was asked what the most astounding fact is, he replied "The atoms in my body can be traced all the way back to the crucibles of stars, cooking light elements into heavy elements. These elements explode, scattering their enriched guts across the universe, gradually forming dense clouds which become planets. These planets form the compounds carbon, nitrogen and oxygen, producing the perfect cocktail for life to exist. And through the beautiful process of evolution here we stand. It's important we not only know that we are in this universe, part of this universe, but most importantly the universe is within us. When most people look at the night sky they feel small, but I feel big, because my atoms came from those stars. It gives us a sense of connection and that's all we want in life – to feel connected."

The creator of the Google Glass project, Tom Chi, takes this a step further. In a video he looks at the recycling of atoms in our bodies and goes into further detail as to why and how we are all connected. Chi explains that everyday we approximately take in about 2 and a half kilograms of water and food as well as exchanging almost a kilogram of air. This means that for most of us 7% of what we thought was us will no longer be us tomorrow. That's roughly the mass of our arms, so every day we are losing an arm load of who we are and gaining a new one. This means that every fortnight the entire mass of our bodies will have been completely exchanged. Just like in the THINK chapter our sense of 'I' hasn't changed, yet in some sense we are completely different to who we were 2 weeks ago and over a year we are most definitely different. This means we are in a constant state of inner-becoming with the Earth. Winds take approximately 4-5 days to reach the other side of the planet, meaning that the very breath you're taking now could have been a partial breath of someone on the opposite side of the world. In less than a week's time your exhale could be doing its part to become a tree in a different country. This isn't just a theory – this is exactly second by second what is happening.

Physically we are interconnecting with nature, with organisms and with conscious beings. Like Neil deGrasse-Tyson says; we're not just part of the universe, the universe is in us. Tom Chi's description reminds us not that we're on the planet, but that we are the planet.

Science can often seem cold and clinical, but once we understand these truths on a deep emotional level it's impossible not to feel like we're part of something more and to feel connected. The next time you can feel the technostress creeping up in your bucket embrace nature, breathe it in and remind yourself of the world's most astounding fact.

Mind/Body Connection

One of the primary reasons that our bodies have suffered from lifestyle choices in comparison to other periods in history is that we have stopped listening to it. I've mentioned before that when we experience pain in our bodies we tackle the symptoms but not the source. Let's take a look at what pain actually is. Most people believe that pain happens in the body but just like reality itself, pain happens in the mind. Pain itself is a symptom, it is our body's way of trying to send a conscious message that will make us change our behaviour so that we eliminate the cause. The moment we cover up the symptoms, whether that's through a tablet or gel, we need to remember we haven't for a second stopped the pain, we've just temporarily stopped the message getting through.

As children my sister and I lived opposite a set of terraced houses. One morning as we were looking through the window at them we could see a postman trying to deliver a message through a neighbour's letterbox. The letterbox was jammed so he rang the doorbell but no-one answered. He then started knocking, but no-one heard him and so he knocked harder. 30 seconds later he started knocking on the windows, yet no-one was answering. He wondered over to the side of the road where he picked up pieces of gravel and started throwing them at the bedroom window to see if he could get a response. My sister and I started laughing because it was the most eager postman we'd ever seen! We started joking and imagining him to climb over the garden fence to knock on the back windows of their house. Failing that what would he do next? Would he break into their shed, pull out a ladder and start to climb up to their bedroom window shouting "Got a delivery!"? For years we referred to this man as the eager postman. We laughed at the idea of this couple in bed being woken up in this terrified manner by the dreaded myth of the eager postman who simply just wanted to give them a letter. Clearly he hadn't gotten the hint when the couple ignored the ringing doorbell! But our bodies too act like the myth of the eager postman. If we try to ignore a message coming through from our bodies, it will find a louder and more obtrusive way to get the message through to you until it's so loud that you can no longer afford to ignore it. The truth is with the postman, if the couple had just opened the door he would have left them alone!

Our pain, emotionally and physically, needs to be seen as eager postmen trying to send messages... if we ignore something that bothers us emotionally, if we try to ignore that it's there, the emotional mind will find another way to show us there's a problem. Think of the emotional mind like a 5-year-old child. If it doesn't get its way it will eventually throw a tantrum. There's two ways to do this. Either we can be the strict parent of our body and shut the tantrum down (which can work but has very low success rates) or we can choose to cease ignoring it and address what the tantrum is *really* about. Think to a time when you've been angry in the past, fuming, raging and we kept trying to suppress it by telling ourselves "don't be angry, don't be angry, don't be angry". Now what is wrong with this strategy? First of all we are focusing on what we don't want, which of course only brings energy to that thought tenfold. Secondly, we're ignoring something that is actually there – remember the Primal Life Method isn't about positive thinking, it's about playing the game of life intelligently. Ignoring something that is existing is not going to allow us to change our reality, it simply means we're kidding ourselves into a temporary fantasy. We need to see things as they are, not worse than they are, but as they are. When we do the Sparkling Moment a lot of people think we're putting on the rose-tinted glasses when actually we're doing the exact opposite. The Sparkling Moment allows us to see things how they are. The truth of the matter is that in this day and age everything moment to moment is more or less pretty darn good and it is very unlikely our survival is actually

239

being threatened. Putting on the green filters (seeing things as they are) simply sheds a light on this fact.

An extreme example of listening to our emotions can be seen in the popular TED talk by Eleanor Longden. In it Eleanor tells the story of when she started hearing voices, physically started hearing them and of course she thought she was crazy. At first these voices would describe things she was doing such as "she is leaving the room" or "she is opening the door". Slowly the voices would get louder and more aggressive and she'd need to win their approval for them to stop. She'd have to do things while at college like pour water over her lecturer. Eventually the voices were telling her to kill herself. When listening to this story it screams Schizophrenia and Psychosis, however the incredible point comes up that a large part of her pain was due to ignoring the voices and suppressing them, which made them worse. What she eventually did was, rather than fighting the voices, she started to listen to them and what they were actually trying to tell her. What she realised was that the voices were simply trying to give her messages of her emotional state. If the voices said "don't leave the house" then she understood that she was feeling unsafe and could do something about it. By interpreting the meaning of the messages that were trying to come through she no longer needed psychiatric help. She had built a mind-body connection.

So many of us are scared to listen to the parts of us that are in pain. It's only when we look at it and see it for what it truly is that it will disappear. A little bit like the eager postman you only have to experience a second of discomfort by opening the door for the postman to go away, as opposed to ignoring him and waiting for him to show up in a scarier place.

Sometimes when we are feeling insecure, annoyed, upset or anxious we need to remember that the limbic system (Chimp, emotional mind) is trying to allow its voice to be heard. From now on, instead of trying to cage it, I want you to listen to it. By asking the right questions you'll allow the Chimp to have its say and be able to acknowledge the issue. Doing this will let the Chimp simmer down. This is going to feel alien at first but I assure you that this is just another habit, that once added to your toolbox, will allow you to have so much more self-control and a lot less uncomfortable moments.

One of the techniques we can use can be found in Byron Katie's *The Works*. By simply asking 4 questions it will allow us to listen to the Chimp, question the Chimp and simmer it. Let's use an example:

A friend makes a joke at our expense and this upsets us. The Chimp pops up its head with an insecure response because remember, the Chimp isn't evil – it's a 5-year-old child that's been wired to see things negatively for your survival. It says "Sam doesn't like me"… Now before we enter an out of control negative loop let's embrace the belief that "Sam doesn't like me" and ask it this question:

"Is it true?"

A note to add here is it's quite usual for us to not want to engage the Chimp because it feels like we're being pathetic." Surely I'm pathetic if I think my best friend doesn't like me because of just one thing they said….?" I'm going to make it clear for you now, we're human and all have insecurities no matter how silly they may seem sometimes. If you want to use the word "pathetic" "stupid" "silly" I can assure you it is a lot more foolish to ignore these niggles and let them build up in your stress bucket and ruin your day, indirectly contributing to ruining the rest of your week or beyond. Let's tackle these moments when they come up, when they're just still niggles, rather than having to battle the aftermath which will feel like a tidal wave. So, first question: "Is it true?" Now very often in these moments if you genuinely ask that question you'll realise it is not true and the Chimp will settle back down. But if the answer is "Yes, it is true" you need to ask it question 2, which is:

"Can I know it's 100% true?"

As we already know, we're not mind readers or clairvoyants. We know that meaning is subjective no matter how real we believe otherwise, so the answer has to be "No". We can never know 100% that this is absolutely true. Let's ask it question 3:

"Who am I/how do I feel if I believe this is true?"

You may answer "Well, actually I feel angry, insecure, negative in my thinking, I become a worse friend, in fact it brings out the worst in me"

So, the 4th question is:

"Who am I/how do I feel when I think this isn't true?"

You may reply with "Well actually I enjoy my day, I feel good, I become a better friend, I enjoy my own company much more".

If we realise by dropping the negative thought that we feel better and can give more from that then we can find the empowering belief and enforce it using the belief table I taught in the THINK chapter e.g. Sam does like me and here are all the reasons why... and find as many legs as possible to strengthen that table.

The next time we start to feel worried, sad, down, fatigued, lonely or any emotion that represents a flavour of suffering to us, instead of using a negative question that puts us in a negative state, we can use an empowering question to diagnose and solve the problem and put us back to the right biochemical balance. Questions such as "What's my body trying to tell me?", "What's my Chimp trying to save me from?". From this we may realise the answer is simpler than we first thought e.g. "I feel lonely and bored because my body's trying to remind me I haven't connected with my tribe for a while". Acknowledging this will allow us to actively interact with others as opposed to ignoring the loneliness and use a drug or a type of food to give us a dopamine or oxytocin spike that temporarily masks the symptom.

Strengthening the mind/body connection isn't just useful for emotions, it's useful for physical sensations too. If it's been a long day at work and we haven't been moving we feel tired when we leave the office. We can start to understand from the Primal Life Method that our body isn't saying 'I need to sit down', it's saying 'I need to move'!

The most common question you'll find yourself asking if you're not feeling at your peak is "Am I biochemically sober?" and 99 times out of 100 I can assure you one of these principles isn't being followed. The 7 steps of the Primal Life Method are all terrific strategies to strengthen our mind/body connection. The moment we change our breathing we can immediately feel a change in our body. Meditation allows us to open our awareness of the sensations in our body including our thoughts. Moving our bodies aerobically or through resistance allows us to connect with our biomechanics and hormonal processes. Fuel is a terrific way to connect to our bodies, "Do I feel this last meal cleansed me or clogged me?", "Do I have brain fog? Clearly that's inflammation so I need to stop eating that food and cherish my body". As we already know if we invest even just an hour into our bodies every day our body pays us back tenfold. The cold is an extremely powerful way to build upon that core connection, in fact it was only when I learnt to endure the cold that I truly learnt to listen to my body properly.

Connect with your tribe, connect with the world around you, connect with nature, but more importantly connect with yourself.

<u>CONNECT Chapter Summary</u>

- Our ancestors used to spend all their time with their tribe ranging from 50-150 people. There was a high dependence on one another to survive which promoted fierce egalitarianism.

- When we interact with people we release the hormone oxytocin in our body which increases levels of trust, empathy and connection between individuals and groups.

- It is built within our genetics that in times of crisis we band together to form communities and adopt the tribal egalitarian approach – rates of depression, suicide, crime and mania all decrease.

- Long periods of isolation are easy to do in the 21st century (due to the illusion of community), however it is another evolutionary mismatch that lowers oxytocin levels and triggers a stress response.

- We are genetically "wired" to find a purpose by giving value in our community as a mechanism for survival.

- Our purpose can be unique to us and it can change in time.

- We are the average of the 5 closest people to us (to fit into our tribe we adapt our standards and identity to fit in).

- Unlike hunter gatherer nomads we have the ability to actively surround ourselves with the people we want to be with.

- Through the access of the internet and having expanded our tribe exponentially through social media we also have the illusion of competition, believing we need to buy particular products to fit in with our community.

- Social media, online communities, TV and physical interactions can create an echo chamber that form a fixed sense or reality. In many circumstances it may not be an empowering echo chamber, but we do have the ability to change that.
- Walking in nature has shown to promote lower concentrations of cortisol and reduce blood pressure and pulse rate. Trees secrete a substance called phytoncides to ward off harmful bugs and rot. By soaking in this compound it actually does our body some good.
- Anatomically, physically and biologically we are connected to everything on this planet.
- When we feel emotional or physical pain it's vital we understand that there is something our body is trying to tell us for our benefit. It is important not to suppress or treat the symptom but to listen to the pain so we can take the appropriate action.

REST

"You're not healthy unless your sleep is healthy"

Dr William Dement

The Importance Of Sleep

The quality of our performance, whether that is mental, emotional or physical will be affected by the quality of our sleep. During the FUEL chapter I said depression can be as simple as gut inflammation. Our depression can just as easily be a consequence of sleep deprivation but that is not all that is affected. Just through a lack of sleep we can succumb to other symptoms such as obesity, diabetes, loss of libido and even memory loss. If the quality of our sleep is in danger then so is our immune system. Some studies have shown that just by experiencing one night of sleep deprivation you can become as insulin resistant as a type 2 diabetic. If you look at the list of symptoms I have just mentioned and spread that over months, years or even decades you can see that a lack of sleep is a sure-fire way to kill you quicker and significantly reduce your health span.

I have left rest/sleep for the last step of the Primal Life Method out of habit. I think the Primal Life principles flow well in the order it does: Think, Breathe, Move, Fuel, Cold, Connect, Rest. If we were to prioritise these then sleep would undoubtedly come at the top. For some reason it seems to be one of the qualities that as a society we value the least despite it being crucial to our performance and responsible for the maintenance of so many bodily functions. A study in the medical journal The Lancet showed that individuals who are sleep deprived took 14% longer to complete a task and made 20% more errors than well rested individuals. Imagine if you had a drug that could make you 14% quicker and 20% more accurate with no side-effects... sleep is that drug and it is free, so give yourself that prescription now!

Scientists at Colorado State University in 2008 reported that 98% or more people operate according to 24-hour patterns. This means our circadian rhythms (our body clock) are vital to abide by even down to a genetic level. Before the lightbulb was invented some research suggests that people were sleeping up to 10 hours a night. When the lightbulb was invented it went down to 8 hours. When surveys are conducted nowadays on how long people sleep the average is 7 to 7 and a half hours, meaning many of us are getting up to 30% less recovery time than our bodies are technically used to. This is a huge difference and can lead to a large decrease in our daily performance.

Depending on the light available to us our biochemistry can alter hour by hour. For us to feel sleepy and sleep we must be able to release a chemical called melatonin. The moment we are breaking from a sleep pattern and working when tired, we unbalance our body's circadian rhythm and disrupt our body's ability to release melatonin. Instead of relying on the sun to alter our melatonin like our ancestors, artificial light is consistently throwing us slightly off balance. Even just the red light from a TV on stand-by can cause a fluctuation in our melatonin levels.

There's a particular type of sleep that's more important than any other and you may have heard about it: REM sleep, meaning Rapid Eye Movement. The stress bucket, the hypothetical bucket that stores all our accumulated negative thoughts, is best emptied via REM. Now sleep and REM are quite difficult subjects as it is not easy to tell what's going on when someone is dreaming. However two psychotherapists, Dr Joe Griffin and Dr Ivan Tyrrell studied this in great detail and they referred to it as the Human Givens Approach. The Human Givens Approach is that when we sleep and go into REM we re-run our emotional memories throughout the day into narrative memories, memories we have control over. You will probably be familiar with how this works... Someone says something to you during the day and you can't quite get it out your head. You think about it over and over through the emotional mind, perhaps tell your friend or partner when you get home and they tell you just to forget about it, but you can't. That night you re-run the event in your head whilst sleeping, either as it happened or in metaphor (which is when we dream) and when we wake up we have completely forgotten about the thing that person said. Even if we haven't forgotten we may think 'why do I even let that person bother me?' and get on with our day. All the time we hear the phrase "I'll sleep on it", because when we're sleeping and especially while in REM we bring together details of memories throughout the day, gather the general gist of it and form it into a template so that the next time an event like that happens we can be more prepared.

Like I said at the beginning of this book, I want you to be waking up each morning with a completely empty stress bucket. There's a good chance that you and many others may not be and this is a result of one of two things happening. Either we have gone to bed with a full bucket and as we have tried to empty it has overflowed, causing us to wake up in the middle of the night feeling vigilant and alert. In that state we feel there's no way we can get back to sleep. You'll be aware of this feeling because it'll be different than if you woke up needing the toilet during the night. The other thing that could be happening is you could be oversleeping. Have you ever had it when you went to bed, slept for ages, and woke up shattered? It's because we've spent far too much time in REM trying to clear the bucket. We only spend 20-25% of our time in REM, the main reason being its extremely enervating. Most people think that when we sleep, the brain just calms down and relaxes. When we are in REM the brain has actually kicked up a gear and it's working 4 times as hard. If you were to look at it under an FMRI machine you'd see the brain burning white hot. When we wake up the next day we feel shattered; our body is fine but our brain is not because it's been working double time. When we are feeling tired it's our brain that's feeling depleted of energy, not our body.

Navy Seals commonly refer to a point in exercise called the 40% rule. By this they mean that when you get to the point where you feel you can't go on, you've only actually depleted 40% of the energy in your body, but your brain has sent a warning saying that we could be running low on fuel in the tank, so it starts to send the signal that we could be fatigued. Through the Navy Seals understanding this they're able to push their bodies much further and harder because they know there's at least 60% more in their body and they are not even half way to exhaustion.

To help speed up the whole process of this method I do offer a relaxation CD, available from my website as a paid download or as part of a course package. The way it works is that it takes you into a deeper level of sleep more efficiently so that you can empty your bucket at night. What's the best way to start the day off? It is to have had an incredible sleep the night before. That's what this track is going to do for you! Starting on day 1 of the Primal Life Method you can start the process of emptying your stress bucket at night. I was once told by a 70-year-old woman with insomnia that this CD was better than any sleeping pill she'd ever taken, so stick to it and see for yourself how much of a difference it makes!

Sleep Hacks

I want to share with you some great proven tips for getting better sleep. No matter who we are, chances are we can all do with better sleep. These tips are quick, easy and effective, so let's jump right in.

The first is light. I touched upon this in the previous section but it's time now to emphasise how powerful the evolutionary mismatch of artificial light is and how it has caused modern society to shift. It's something we are surrounded by that our genes were not expecting because our ancestors never had it. The primary culprit... blue light! Blue light is found everywhere: in florescent lit environments, in our TVs, on our laptops and tablets and our mobile phones. These lights stimulate dopamine, one of our happy neurotransmitters. This is great if we want to feel active but if we are stimulating dopamine it means we're inhibiting melatonin. This means a part of our brain is going to be wired while another part just wants to rest for the evening. In his book *Head Strong*, Dave Asprey make a great point which takes us back to our mitochondria - the powerhouses that create energy within our cells, "To process the blue light in LEDs our mitochondria have to produce much more energy, which burns oxygen and stresses the mitochondria in our eyes. This causes the rest of our mitochondria to get stressed including the ones in our brain". Essentially looking at blue light constantly is just another way to reduce the energy in our bodies without getting any benefits from it. Since learning that these blue screens don't give me any benefit whatsoever; the phone, tablet and any electronic system I'm using will always be in constant night mode. This means that light from my screens is being transmitted through an infrared filter, allowing the mitochondria in my eyes, brain and body to take a well-earned rest. I've noticed a huge difference in the quality of my sleep pattern and ability to focus since implementing this change.

Here's a little experiment to try at home; if you take your phone or tablet off of night mode, so it goes back to the blue screen, you'll notice the pain it gives your eyes. The moment you take it back to night mode your eyes will not flinch. You can usually find night mode options in your device settings or you can download free apps such as FLUX and Blue Light Filters. This allows you to adjust the blue light into yellow/red light based on the time of day. As I mentioned before, I personally have mine on constant night mode and advocate this.

The Universities of Pittsburgh and Harvard in 2009 showed there was a correlation between the risk of teenagers developing depression during the next 7 years and the more TV they watched. This doesn't necessarily mean it's the TV they watch that causes this but rather the blue light which causes lack of sleep. As we now know that lack of sleep can cause depression, it becomes obvious why there is a link between the two.

For the next sleep hack let's talk about caffeine. Caffeine doesn't technically give you energy, it masks your fatigue. It's incredible how it does this...

When we've been working throughout the day and our neurons have been firing, they produce a by-product called adenosine. The more we're working and more neurons we're firing, the more adenosine that's in our system. And this can build and build. What the adenosine usually does is it binds with different receptors which sends signals to your body which prompt it to rest, recover and sleep. What caffeine does however is it beats the adenosine to the receptors and acts as a block, so that your brain never gets the signal to take it easy and nod off despite the rest being needed. It's not wise to keep tricking our body into a false sense of endurance thinking that it's ok when really it just needs to rest. Caffeine has a half-life of 5-8 hours, which means if you have a standard coffee in the morning with 250mg of caffeine in it, only half of that will be out of your system by the time you finish work. We can all metabolise caffeine at different rates; some of us can have a cup of coffee at 2pm and have it burnt our system by the early evening. If you're going to take risks with your sleep pattern it's best to test this theory with a doctor rather than assume you metabolise it quickly.

The next hack is our good friend the cold! Our bodies are great at keeping us warm but it's a little more difficult for it to keep us cool. Lots of research has been done into the ideal room temperature for the best sleep and the best temperature has been proven to be 60-68 degrees Fahrenheit (15.5-20 degrees Celsius). If you can't sleep well, get cold and let the cold be your warm friend at night.

The American Academy of Sleep Medicine Research has proven that meditating in the morning helps people sleep better at night. The whole process of creating neural pathways, myelinating the ones we want and removing the ones we don't, allows us to relax and access the present moment quicker. Meditation isn't just for clearing our mind, we can use it as a wonderful off switch too.

And finally... follow the Primal Life Method! Something I'm going to cover in the next chapter is that all these principles intertwine beautifully to complement each other. They get you biochemically sober and give you that better level of clarity, focus, health and happiness that we all want. Following the other 6 principles will in turn give you better sleep. They'll balance out the function of the hormones in your body, send you to bed with less stress in your bucket to begin with, and you can use the resonant rate breathing to sync your electrical rhythms…. You'll be out like a light!

Please don't ever forget the importance of your sleep as it's the most difficult thing to make up for the following day.

REST Chapter Summary

- Sleep affects every aspect of our lives including mental health, physical health, productivity, sex drive, cognitive function and appetite. A lack of sleep can be linked to cancer and memory loss.

- Sleeps sews together the general gist of day to day events in our mind, creating a template that helps us in the future.

- REM sleep empties our stress bucket, but the brain must work extra hard to do this.

- Caffeine doesn't give us energy, rather it masks our fatigue.

- Just like junk food we can have junk light. This predominantly comes from blue LED lights found in laptops, computers, TVs and phone screens. These lights strain our mitochondria and lowers the available energy to us and inhibits melatonin (the hormone needed to regulate our circadian rhythms).

- We can use blue light filters on our screens which turns the screen yellow/red allowing our body to produce melatonin and sleep better.

THE SCIENCE OF HEALTH

"Science is a beautiful gift to humanity; we should not distort it"

A.P.J Abdul Kalam

Bad Science

All the techniques and principles that you've learnt throughout this book have all been scientifically backed. I want to talk to you about that term in more detail because as pure as science is in theory, it can very often be a dogmatic practice that when put into place by researchers can misrepresent the truth. Many of us are willing to hang our beliefs, values and reality on a handful of scientific studies. Just because a research study states that there's a correlation between 2 variables it doesn't mean that variable X caused variable Y. The problem with testing anything, especially people and animals, is that it's near enough impossible to account for all the variables that can affect the result.

Think about how powerful the Placebo Effect is; just by having a completely different subjective point of view, we can objectively alter scientific results. Very often when we're trying to get objective results such as X = Y, what we're not taking into account are the participants subjective thoughts and feelings. Now the Catch 22 that we have with this is it's very difficult (and some would say impossible) to measure subjective feelings objectively. Even the results are supposed to be objectively observed through a subjective point of view (have I lost you yet?!).

This doesn't mean that one day science won't somehow find a way to encompass all these variables when testing participants, but when we're reading medical journals or reading the newspapers that 'studies have shown XYZ' we must at best take that with a pinch of salt, but in most cases deny it completely. The point I'm trying to make here is a big and extremely complex one, so if there's any book that I urge anyone to read when it comes to how scientific research is presented (both to the public and within the scientific community) it would be *Bad Science* by Ben Goldacre.

Ben does a great job as he rips apart the common myths most of us still believe, breaks the fads that get undeserved hype, and cuts through with the best research available on how inaccurate science can really be when put into practice.

At least 33% of studies published in scientific journals aren't true. There will always be a way to nudge the results of an experiment to give us the results we want. A really good quality experiment may be undertaken by a big pharmaceutical company, but Ben shows that even an experiment done at the best quality can be interpreted to show what the scientist was hoping to see.

What I love most about the Primal Life Method is that even when you strip away the scientific evidence which proves it, it is still supercharged logic. The best way for you to know if it's the truth is to test it and see if it works for you. Some could class this as anecdotal evidence but as our health and happiness are anecdotal as a rule, it's the best method we can test to see if this works for you.

TRACKING

"The ultimate measure of a man is not where he stands in moments of comfort and convenience, but where he stands at times of challenge and controversy"

Martin Luther King, Jr

Measuring Outcomes

A message I have been trying to emphasise throughout the whole Primal Life Method is that despite being a map for personal growth in our holistic health and wellness, it is not about positive thinking. When beginning any journey we need to know where our starting point is and this can sometimes be a painful process, but it's necessary. This gives us a true understanding of what our baseline is and the moment we know where we are, the moment we've been bold enough to take this step we can smile, we can pat ourselves on the back and know that as we start this process we're never going to be here again.

When it comes to our mental wellbeing, it is important to have an indication of your improvement. With my clients I end each session with asking them to rate themselves on a scale of 1 to 10 (1 being the worst we could ever feel, 10 being life is just the way we want it to be) in 7 key criteria, which I refer to as your Primal Outcomes. It gives an overall sense of our lifestyle and shows where we need to improve. I then plot the average score of the criteria on a graph for them to get an overall average of how good they're feeling. The 7 criteria are as follows:

Thoughts

How would you rate yourself in your ability to recall positive memories and also have compelling thoughts for the future?

Interactions

What are the qualities of your interactions? Remember, more doesn't necessarily mean better. It really is about quality not quantity.

Activities

What positive activities are you getting involved with? These are activities that help you flourish and can benefit you in some way. For example, playing tennis, stargazing, hiking or playing chess.

Achievement

Your ability to recognise all the things you've achieved and also your ability to move towards achieving new things.

Strengths & Resources

Recognising the strengths and resources that are in you now and your ability to apply them

Confidence

How would you measure your overall confidence? E.g. physical body, social situations, capabilities.

Overall Happiness

How will you know if the Primal Life Method is working for you? Those numbers are going to change in the right direction.

Take a moment now, in fact take a few moments to look at where you are on a scale of 1 to 10 for all those things. Sadly no halves are allowed, it has to be whole numbers. If you're between a 4 or 5 then we'll settle for a 4. If you're a 5 or more for something then excellent, you're already halfway there!

If you're looking at those numbers and thinking "oh my gosh they're so low" it's ok. Just by doing this it's a courageous first step, because we're finally willing to see things how they are, which means we can start changing them. Be prepared to say goodbye to those numbers because we have an exciting journey ahead.

When I start this journey with a new client, a key point that I do insist they understand is that each week over a course of 12 weeks the numbers will not go up consistently. It will likely look like an uphill wave.

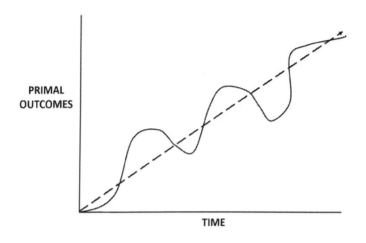

This is how we want the graph to look! Why? Because this isn't just about progressing in our life, it's about growing that resilience too.

The moment we can see immediate changes being made we start to party. Very often during this party when we're least expecting it, life kindly throws us a big curveball. Whether that is through a phone call we weren't expecting, an event on the news, anything out of our control that we had no way to predict - it will knock us back. This happens to all of us.

I had a client who after our initial consultation flew home! He understood how the brain worked, it made sense to him. He came in for his first session a week later and his results on the 7 criteria went up. The following week they jumped up again and he said he felt as if the heaviest burden had just been lifted off of his shoulders. Our third session however, he had to cancel as the previous evening he had taken an overdose in an attempted suicide. It was a harrowing process to have gone through for him, feeling on top of the world for the first time in a long time before having a relapse in his emotions. Thankfully he pushed on and rode through the dips, climbing up the scale. So much so I'm proud to say he has since done bigger and better things!

If we feel like we're stuck in a pit, the first couple of weeks we're progressing is the equivalent of us constructing a rope to climb out of the hole. When we finally climb out of the hole it feels fantastic. The dip will at first feel like someone's just pushed us back in. Of course it will feel terrible as it'll feel like we've made no progress – after all we're back in the hole! However, because we've spent all that time making the rope, the time we spend in that hole will be significantly less. We've already put time into making the tool that will help us get out. This isn't about stopping you from ever having a bad day, it's about having a sturdy coping mechanism to get us out of there quicker and quicker each time until your bad moments start to feel non-existent. The real test of all of this is when the dip comes. The best thing you can do now before you've even started is to prepare for the dip to come.

The biggest mistake most of us make when it comes to making a plan is that we don't prepare for the inevitable obstacles. One of the leading researchers of Positive Psychology, Gabriele Oettingen, gives a great strategy to ensure success when making new goals. She refers to her strategy as WOOP, which stands for Wish, Outcome, Obstacle and Plan.

Wish = What are you after? What is it you want to achieve in the next week, month or year?

Outcome = What's the number one benefit you would experience as a result of this?

Obstacle = What obstacle within you is going to stop you achieving that wish? I'll say that again... What obstacle *within you* is going to stop you achieving that wish?

Plan = What's your strategy to get over that obstacle? What's the most effective thing you can do? "*If* X happens *then I* will Y".

Give WOOP a go yourself. Name your wish in 3-6 words. Just relax and let it come to you. For example:

Your wish could be to start the Primal Life 12 week course.

The outcome is you'll feel happier and healthier for it.

An obstacle is that you could lose motivation.

Your plan could be – "*If I* lose motivation *then I* will re-visit my notes on why I'm at threshold and re-watch my favourite videos from the course again."

I always want you to say your plan out loud to yourself once you've written it down to re-enforce this strategy to your subconscious mind and start that feedback loop.

Now why is the Primal Life Method online course 12 weeks long? Because that is how long it takes to build a habit. What you may find is that it doesn't take very long for you to reach an 8 or 9 out of 10. Getting to where you want to be in your wellbeing isn't actually too difficult. It's keeping you there where the real work starts! I could have made this programme a 30-day intense course but as I've said before and I'll say again... this isn't the Primal Month Method, it's the Primal Life Method.

For it to be 12 weeks long you will excel upwards, most likely with some dips along the way. However, it's also likely that you will hit a plateau.

I have seen clients 10 weeks into the course and their Primal Outcomes are 9/10 but they'll suddenly start to consistently go back to an 8. Why? Because their goalposts have shifted and they've jumped up to a whole new standard. I had one client who came to see me and a 9/10 for her would be to remove the existential crisis she was having. The first thing we did was obviously re-frame the question into the positive so there was actually something to aim towards, and then got to work. Within no time at all she reached that goal and was more often than not a 10/10. But this started to drop back to a 9/10 when she realised she was capable of so much more and the next level for her wasn't to live without an existential crisis, it was to double the size of her business in the next 12 months! The beauty of personal growth is we can never get bored as the growth never stops. There's 3 ways we can approach a plateau:

Dabbler

Hypothetically, you may see your progress slowly but surely increase, maybe with slight small dips along the way, but generally you're doing well and stay around a 7 or 8. A Dabbler in any progression at this point will likely give up. You enjoyed the growth, enjoyed the feeling of progress, got to a particular level to which you plateaued and stopped. You'll move onto something else that you really enjoy to get the same feeling of progress again. There's nothing particularly wrong about being a dabbler, it just means you'll have tried and tested lots of different things to find what works best for you. This can make you a very interesting person but you never truly become the master of anything.

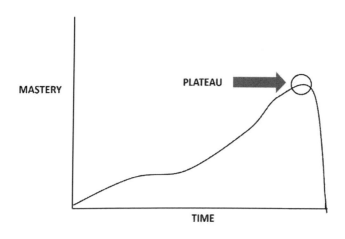

The Stressed Achiever

The same progress happens as the Dabbler and you hit a plateau. However, you decide to become a master and try Plan A, but it doesn't work. So you try Plan B, but that doesn't work either. However, you're an achiever so you keep going until you reach Plan T and finally move to the next level. You by-pass the plateau, and all that stress was worth it because you're that one step closer to mastery.

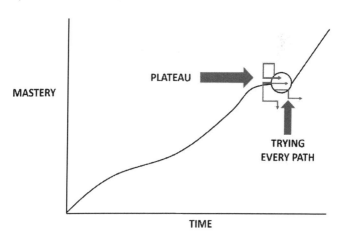

The Modeller

With the same graph as the other two, low and behold you hit a plateau. However instead of dabbling and moving onto the next interest, instead of by-passing the plateau while having a cardiac arrest to do so, you'll step back and say (in the voice of Sir Anthony Hopkins) "Ah, a plateau... I pre-empted this day. 7 billion people exist on this planet and therefore I am certain that someone has been at this plateau before, but who? I shall find them, I shall ask them, I shall offer them value and in return they shall part with their wisdom so I can continue on my path for mastery".

If we really want to explore what we are capable of and are packed with the curiosity to find out what else we have to give, then the Modeller's approach is the smartest path. It's for reasons like this I give free access to the Primal Life community on Facebook. Not only does this give you an empowering echo chamber and make it easier for you to find a new tribe but it also allows you to have access to others who can help you by-pass your plateau. On top of this it can give you the rewarding sense of contribution when you help others pass theirs.

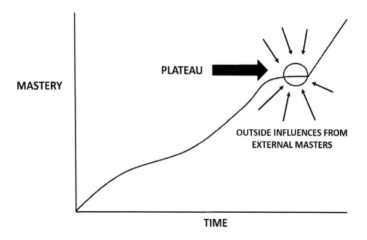

PRIMAL PRACTICE

"We are what we repeatedly do. Excellence is therefore not an act but a habit"

Aristotle

Morning Routine

Just like meditation, the majority of the world's top performers share something else in common: a morning routine. There's a popular quote 'If you win the morning, you win the day'. Most of us if we're working probably have some sort of morning routine, whether that's cursing our alarm clock, dribbling toothpaste down our chin, falling into a shower, or drinking a cup of coffee while half asleep.

Very often the idea of building a habit or morning routine seems impossible, yet it is something we do everyday without thinking, like the things I've just mentioned. You wouldn't class showering in the morning as a habit, would you? You don't have to do it, it's just something you learnt when you were younger and it became second nature. Well, you can do this with anything.

If we want to have a day where we're feeling on top of the world and our neurotransmitters are working within the realms of biochemical sobriety, then let's set ourselves up for it as opposed to leaving it up to chance.

Barack Obama always started every day in the White House with a 45-minute run on a treadmill. This was his unbending routine and something he was relentless about. Tony Robbins always starts the day with a cold plunge. Ray Dalio practices transcendental meditation every morning. The first thing Arianna Huffington does upon waking up is to take a minute to breathe deeply and cultivate gratitude.

Which of the Primal Life principles (it could be all of them) would you implement in your morning routine? I will normally do 6 (it's difficult to bond with my community from my bed!). I'll start with 3 sets of the yogic breathing, drink a litre of water and head to the gym. After I've moved my body and if I have access to a cold shower I'll take it.

I then spend 10-20 minutes meditating to practice mindfulness and cultivate gratitude. I will then write in my journal and finish it off with some Sparkling Moments. Depending on when I'd last eaten I might have a salad for the first meal of my day. Not every day will be like this. Sometimes things don't go to plan, but I do whatever I can to reboot my body and mind before I've even started work. I am already on peak, feeling great in my body and mental outlook before I've even left the house for the day.

What will be your inflexible principles that you can add to your routine? Will you start with the resonant breaths like Ariana Huffington and priming your mind for the day through gratitude? Or will it be a quick 30-60 second cold shower after washing your body? The more principles you integrate into your day-to-day life, and the earlier you can start them, the better. Having a morning routine using the Primal Life principles allows you to be sober for longer and start the day as the best you.

Time isn't an excuse not to do these principles. If the world's most prominent sports athletes and CEOs of the biggest organisations can spare 10 minutes for themselves in the morning, then so can you. If you can't spare just 10 minutes then you don't have a life!

The Talker & The Doer

I've bombarded you with a lot of information in this book; it's a lot of theory to take in and a whole new way to look at life. But as I've mentioned before, all of the hours you've spent learning this truly are at best a waste of time if you don't put any of it into practice. Remember the Tim Ferris quote "all the knowledge in the world and $4 will get you a cup of coffee at Starbucks". The most common thing we want to do when we've learnt something (especially when it's as big as this) is to go out there and start talking about it. "Wow, look at all these cool facts that explain the way we think, act and feel. Look at the changes we can make in our lives! I can't wait to tell everyone I know about this!" Well, guess what!? I don't want you to tell a soul about this. Sure, tell them about Lester Savage and the Primal Life Method, but I want you to refrain from being the talker and instead, let people simply know through your physiology, from the shape of your body, the language you use and the way that you give that you are a doer. When you do the work that's involved in the principles here I promise you, you won't need to say anything out there as people will see your results and approach you. They'll see from the way your body is changing, or even the smallest things like the way you keep calm when bad moments arise. It's these things that will allow people to know that you've become biochemically sober. We don't just need teachers in life, we need examples. When people can see you doing incredible feats with the cold, showing extraordinary emotional resilience, and having an abundance of joy and energy throughout the day, you'll be the example people need to change themselves. If you're not doing it for you, do it for them. If you feel you've learnt a lot now, that's terrific but I can assure you the real learning doesn't start until you apply this.

This isn't about the theory, it's about the practice. I cannot tell you the power between knowing something logically and knowing this on an emotional level. We logically know that all these things separately make sense. Of course we should be eating better, of course we should be moving our body and of course we should all be having more sleep. Maybe I shouldn't be slouched over my desk all day and maybe my outlook has been more negative than usual.

It's by combining these principles that you'll really get an effect that will change life for you. Each of these principles affect the other: If you're not running on the right fuels, your body won't move effectively and the way that you move your body of course affects how hungry you are. Even the quality of sleep you have can affect your appetite and if we haven't had enough REM we're waking up with more stress in our body affecting the way we're thinking. If we're thinking negatively and releasing those spikes of cortisol our breathing will change, this lowers the amount of energy available to us for moving our body. If we're not exposing our bodies to differing temperatures that's going to affect our immune system which can affect the quality of our sleep. It is difficult to feel great when we're feeling ill. When we're ill we can't exercise or think as clearly. You can see that all these principles create a wide web that all connect with each other and it is by doing all 7 of these that we become biochemically sober.

If I'm ever not feeling myself, if for some reason I'm not at peak, the first question I'll always ask is "Am I biochemically sober? Have I done all 7 of these steps?" and every single time it's a no. This also goes for every client I've worked with. If people are feeling down, upset, flagging in energy, there will always be 1 or 2 of these principles they're not doing or possibly even more. I remember once throughout the day I wasn't feeling myself, I'd done my breathing in the morning and felt clear... but that only lasted for about 2 hours. I'd meditated and journaled and for an hour felt a great sense of bliss. But that also faded. I went through the checklist: I had moved my body, the fuel I was putting in it was fantastic, I'd interacted with friends and saw clients (doing something in line with my purpose) yet for some reason I still didn't feel like me. I kept feeling tired, I could feel stress in my body and before I knew it I started to feel negative. By the end of the day, for the first time in over a year I actually felt a little bit paranoid. I went through the checklist again.... "Is there a principle I haven't done?", and then I realised that for the previous 3 days, despite doing the Primal Life Method, due to the events that were going on at the time I'd been getting approximately 6 hours of sleep every night. We know we're meant to be getting 7-10 hours per night minimum! This meant that in 3 nights/4 days I'd affectively gone a whole night without sleep. I hadn't been clearing my stress bucket appropriately. So that night, in my paranoid state, I kept thinking over and over again (because clearly I was working in the limbic system/emotional mind) "Am I really thinking like this just because I haven't slept properly?". That night I went to bed early and had a great sleep – clearly my body needed it. When I woke the next morning I felt terrific. Even with logically knowing the importance of sleep, it wasn't until I experienced that event of feeling anxious and then having that anxiety cure itself through a good night's sleep that I emotionally understood its importance.

If you're struggling with being able to do one of these principles then do the others first. As they're all linked, it will make it so much easier to do the 7th when you've already improved your biochemistry through the other 6. If sleep is something you've always struggled with I can assure you that once you abide by the other 6 principles you will see significant improvements. If you struggle to think clearly and you feel it's hard to escape that negative loop then by focusing on the other 6 principles it will give you the best fighting chance. It may be that you have inflammation and doing these other principles will help reduce that - giving you access to stronger and more resilient neural pathways. Don't just take my word for it – test it and see for yourself.

Something I do think is vital to add is something that is not spoken about enough within personal development materials. One of my mentors once told me "It's only a problem if it's a problem". When he first said this, I thought I must have misheard him as the saying doesn't quite sound right. But I had heard him correctly, he really did mean it. It's only a problem if it's a problem. What he meant by this was that we should only ever make changes in our lives if staying the way we are is causing us suffering. Very often in personal development and in the media, we're being told that we "need to have something" if we want to be playing the game of life at a particular standard. 'If you don't have a 6 pack yet then it's a problem' 'If you're not travelling around the world in your free time then it's a problem' 'If you're not having wild sex every day of your life then it's a problem'. The Primal Life Method is in no way a map on how to live, it's simply a set of tools that you can use at your discretion that gives you a path to making a better you. What you may find is that you only need to follow 4 of these principles to be feeling spectacular, in which case that's great. You may feel like you don't need to do the breathing every day, but perhaps every other day. Instead of a daily ritual, cold showers might just be a wonderful antidote to a hangover. You can use this method as much or as little for what's right for you. I have spoken a lot about living life at a certain standard and something that I've made the best effort to make clear throughout this book is that no-one dictates the standard but you.

I remember a lady at one of my seminars who felt like she wanted to be more productive. In fact her very words were "I always feel like I need to be more productive". When we delved deeper into *why* she felt she needed to be more productive it turned out that she thought this was a quality that was

273

expected of her. I asked her if this was a problem for her or could be a problem, to which she replied "no". It turned out that all she needed was to give herself the permission to feel comfortable with her own decisions. By creating a negative echo chamber for herself she was made to feel inadequate about something that she was perfectly fulfilled with. As I said at the beginning, take what works for you and leave what doesn't. Her current level of productivity wasn't a problem, so... it wasn't a problem.

The same goes for enjoying everything and needing nothing. This isn't about living a life of guilt-free hedonism: seeing every country, learning every language, tasting every food, exploring every sexual position, accruing every hobby and collecting every possession. It is about living life on your terms and giving yourself permission to enjoy it all but not need it all. Being biochemically sober is just that terrific first step to taking responsibility for your own wellbeing.

PRIMAL PRACTICE Chapter Summary

- All 7 of the Primal Life principles interlink and influence the other.
- To really know if we are progressing and staying on top of any aspect of our lives we must regularly measure our outcomes.
- Build a great morning routine - all the greatest peak performers have one.
- There are 3 styles that most of us adopt for mastery: dabbler, stressed achiever, modeller.
- Don't talk, do! Don't be a teacher, be an example. This is what others will need to see in order for you to help them transform too.
- It's only a problem if it's a problem. Change only on your terms by recognising the best path for you. It's how you create the most value over all which matters. Things are only an issue if your current situation is making you suffer.
- Enjoy Everything, Need Nothing!

Glossary

Achievement – Something accomplished with a special effort, great courage and sometimes with superior ability

Aerobic – Moving with free oxygen available

Aerobic threshold – The highest amount of heart beats per minute before we cross into an anaerobic sugar burning zone

Amygdala – Centre and most influential area of the limbic system acting like a health and safety officer of our mind, used heavily in our perception of fear

Anaerobic – Moving without free oxygen available causing lactate to form in the body

Auto Immune disease – When process of inflammation begins attacking healthy cells

Autophagy – Natural, regulated, destructive mechanism of the cell that disassembles unnecessary or dysfunctional components

BDNF (Brain Derivative Neurotropic Factor) – Protein responsible for promoting the survival, growth, maturation and maintenance of neurons

Biochemically Sober – When we're releasing a steady flow of empowering hormones and neurotransmitters that make us feel happier and contribute to our overall sense of wellbeing

Biochemistry – Chemical processes within and relating to living organisms e.g. functions occurring within the immune system, metabolism and brain etc.

Blood sugar level – Amount of glucose present in the blood

Breath Awareness – Bringing conscious awareness to the quality of your breath

Brown Adipose Tissue/Brown Fat – Fat on the body used to transfer food into heat

Calorie – The amount of heat that will raise the temperature of 1 gram of water from 14.5°c to 15.5°c

Cell Apoptosis – Programmed cell death

Cold Thermogenesis – Actively using a cold climate/environment so the body is forced to produce heat

Consciously Breathing – Consciously changing the depth, frequency and power of your breath to induce a physiological response

Cortisol – A steroid hormone responsible for regulating functions in the body such as our immune system and metabolism. Plays a key role in the body's response to stress

Courage – A state of mind that allows us to complete actions while feeling fear

Cruciferous Vegetables – Vegetables such as cabbage, kale, bok choy, broccoli -whose flowers have four petals and look like a cross shape

Dabbler – Someone who stops progressing and moves on when they've reached a plateau

Dopamine – A Neurotransmitter that helps control the brain's reward and pleasure centres. It can also help regulate movement and emotional responses

Emotional mind/limbic system/chimp/inner child – Area of the brain responsible for primitive behaviour linked to survival and reproduction

Epigenetics – The change in an organism due to a change in gene expression (genes turned on and off) as opposed to an alteration of the genetic code

Estrogen – The primary female sex hormone

Eustress – A mild stress on the body that allows it to react positively

Evolutionary Mismatch – When our 200,000 year old biology comes into conflict with a style of modern day living that can cause our mind and body harm e.g. having an abundance in sugar, being easily isolated

Fast Acting Carbohydrates – A food with a high GI (above 55)

Fat Burning Hero – Someone who uses fat as their primary food source instead of sugar

Frontal lobe/you/human/Intellectual mind – Responsible for important cognitive skills e.g. communication, it is the control panel/boss of our personality

Fructose – A sugar found in fruit

Fuel – The food and drink we consume that acts as a source or inhibitor for our energy

Fulfilment – A state or quality that recognises completion or realisation

Gene LCT – A gene that when expressed makes the enzyme lactase

Gluten – A type of storage protein found in may grains

Glycemic Index (GI) – A scale of 1-100 that ranks to what extent carbohydrates raise blood sugar levels

Gut Microbiome/Flora – Complex community of microorganisms such as base bacteria, fungi, yeasts that line our digestive tracts and help with most biological processes including digestion

Gut/Second Brain – Area responsible for digestive qualities and manufacturing up to 90% of the serotonin and up to 70% of our immune system regulation

HDL (good) Cholesterol – Helps remove bad cholesterol by moving it to the liver to be broken down

HGH – Human Growth Hormone

Hippocampus – Found in limbic system and holds many long-term memories, responsible for primitive behavioural patterns and involved in spatial awareness

Hyperthermic conditioning – Heat exposure such as a sauna

Hypothalamus – Regulates chemicals in the body and mind

I – The awareness which we relate to being us

Immune System – The bodily functions and processes that involve protecting us from illnesses by destroying pathogens and removing toxins

Inflammation – A biological response of body tissues due to pathogens, damaged cells and irritants etc.

Inflammatory Cytokine – A type of signalling molecule used promoting inflammation

Insulin Growth Factor 1 (IGF1) – A hormone that plays an important part in childhood growth

Intermittent Fasting/Time restricted eating – Fasting for a period of time e.g. 12-18 hours and eating within a minimised time window e.g. 6-12 hours

Lactase – An enzyme that is essential in the digestion of milk

Lactose – A type of sugar found in milk

LDL (bad) Cholesterol – A lipoprotein that contributes to fatty build ups in the arteries (atherosclerosis) which can increase risk of heart attacks etc.

Lectin – Evolved as a natural defence in plants in order to deter predators from eating them. Often referred to as an anti-nutrient as they can reduce the body's ability to absorb nutrients

Left Frontal Cortex – The executive function of us. The part of us that allows for differentiating between conflicting thoughts and what is good and bad. It is the 'boss' of the brain that holds our source of logic and is generally very positive

Logical Levels – Depths of change available to us that allow us to change our circumstance. The deeper the change, the easier it is to alter occurrences outside of that

Luteinising Hormone (LH) – A hormone that helps regulate ovulation and is used in testosterone secretion

Lymphatic System – Series of thin vessels responsible for 70% of the body's detox system

Magnesium – A mineral that helps ensure the parathyroid gland (produces hormones that help with bone health) works efficiently

Melatonin – A hormone secreted by the pineal gland in the brain. It helps regulate other hormones and maintains the body's circadian rhythm. The circadian rhythm is an internal 24-hour "clock" that plays a critical role in when we fall asleep and when we wake up. When it is dark, your body produces more melatonin

Miracle Question – Invention of Insoo Kim Berg that helps guide us from an emotion, to a realistic action we can take to increase the momentum of our progress

Mitochondria – Organelles (organs inside cells) that act as power plants in our body creating ATP (the currency of our body's energy)

Mitochondrial Biogenesis – A process where cells increase the mass of their mitochondria

Modeller – Someone who models their behaviour on successful predecessors in order to effortlessly move past plateaus

Neural Network - A series of interconnected neurons whose activation defines a recognisable linear pathway contributing to our perception of reality

Neuron - A nerve cell (electrically excitable cell) that receives transmits and processes electrical information. They are the primary component of the brain, spinal cord and autonomic nervous system

Neuroplasticity – The "muscle building" phenomenon in the mind that allows us to strengthen and weaken connections in our brain. In essence, it moulds like plasticine and changes over time

Neurotransmitter – A chemical messenger that allows for the transmission of impulses between neurons, muscle cells and gland cells

Noradrenalin/Norepinephrine – A neurotransmitter triggered within the stress response that helps with clear thinking, focus and vigilance

Nucleus Accumbens – Part of the reward system in the brain that plays an important role in processing and reinforcing brain stimuli

Omega 3 – Essential fatty acid used in the reduction of inflammation. May help lower the risk of some chronic diseases such as cancer, heart disease, and arthritis

Omega 6 – Essential fatty acid used in the promotion of inflammation

Osteoporosis – A condition that weakens bones, making them fragile and more likely to break

Oxytocin – A hormone that acts as a neurotransmitter that helps regulate social interaction and sexual reproduction. Oxytocin plays a key role in empathy, generosity and orgasms

Parasympathetic Nervous System – Part of the body's autonomic nervous system responsible for looking after your body during rest and recuperation

Potassium – A mineral that helps balance fluids in the body and helps with heart muscle

Primal Outcomes – The 7 key criteria on which we measure our progress each week

Primatology – The scientific study of primates

REM Sleep – Rapid Eye Movement sleep. A form of sleep that is commonly associated with dreaming

Resonant Rate Breathing – A rate of breathing that allows the electrical rhythms of your brain, heart and lungs to synchronise (generally breathing between 3.5 to 6 breaths per minute)

Reticular Activating System – A networking of nerve pathways in the brain stem connecting subconscious activities to our conscious mind, mediating our overall level of consciousness (what's represented to us/what we focus on).

Serotonin – A neurotransmitter that plays a key role in mood balance, happiness and anxiety. It is linked to high and low levels of serotonin

Shinrin Yoku – Taking in the forest or forest bathing

Slow Acting Carbohydrates – Carbohydrates with a low GI (55 or below)

Sodium Chloride – Salt, a mineral that helps keep the fluid in the body balanced and can help increase the permeability of cells

Sparkling Moment – An exercise that allows us to recall positive moments in the past that in turn "exercises" the left frontal cortex

State – A combination of our internal representations, our behaviours and our physiology that changes our outlook and sense of wellbeing

Strength - The presence of abundant energy - a compacity and reserve to be a force in your world. It's inclusive of health and at the same time so much more. It's being healthy and flowing with energy, power and confidence

Stress Bucket – The theoretical place where our negative thoughts are stored and accumulated

Stressed Achiever – Someone who tried every available avenue before finally breaking through a plateau to achieve mastery

Superhuman fuel – The Primal Life recommended best foods list

Superhuman kryptonite – The Primal Life recommended worst poisons list

Supplements – Another way of adding vitamins, minerals, fibre, amino acids and fatty acids to your diet

Sympathetic Nervous System – Part of the body's autonomic nervous system responsible for stimulating the fight/flight response

Testosterone – The Primary male sex hormone also used in the promotion of body hair, muscle and bone mass

The Primal Life Method – A seven step programme that allows a holistic transformation through changing a person's biochemistry

The Swish Technique – NLP technique that allows to remove the compulsions we wish to get rid of

Threshold – A state of being where we feel change must occur, that change is us, and that it has to happen now

TNF-Alpha – Example of an inflammatory cytokine used within most diseases

Trans fats – An unsaturated fat, also known as hydrogenated fats as they contain long hydrocarbon chains which give them desirable properties for most food businesses

Tummo Meditation – Tummo meaning "inner fire". A form of meditation that focuses on using breathing as a way to move energy through channels in the body to heat it up

White Adipose Tissue/White Fat – Used to store energy

White Blood Cells – Cells of the immune system that are involved in protecting the body against both infectious disease and foreign invaders

Source Notes

THINK

A Guide to the Bodhisattva's Way of Life - Shantideva

A user's guide to the brain – John Ratey

Awaken the Giant Within: How to Take Immediate Control of Your Mental, Emotional, Physical and Financial Destiny! – Anthony Robbins

Buddha's Brain: The Practical Neuroscience of Happiness, Love & Wisdom - Rick Hanson and Richard Mendius

Change Your Brain, Change Your Life – Dr Daniel Amen

Get the Life You Want: The Secrets to Quick and Lasting Life Change with Neuro-Linguistic Programming - Dr Richard Bandler

Happy: Why More or Less Everything is Absolutely Fine – Derren Brown

How to lift depression …Fast (The Human Givens Approach) – Dr Joe Griffin and DR Ivan Tyrrell

How to Transform Your Life: A Blissful Journey – Geshe Kelsang Gyatso

Jordan Peterson Explains Self-Authoring (from Joe Rogan Experience #877). [online] Available at: https://www.youtube.com/watch?v=RoGdMpdZXzs [Accessed 6 Feb. 2018]

Letters from a Stoic – Seneca

Man's Search for Meaning – Viktor E. Frankl

Meditations – Marcus Aurelius

Sapiens: A Brief History of Humankind - Noah Yuval Harari

Selling With NLP: Revolutionary New Techniques That Will Double Your Sales Volume – Kerry L. Johnson

Talent is Overrated: What Really Separates World-Class Performers from Everybody Else – Geoff Colvin

The Brain: The Story of You – David Eagleman

The Chimp Paradox: The Mind Management Programme to Help You Achieve Success, Confidence and Happiness – Dr Steve Peters

The Daily Stoic Journal: 366 Days of Writing and Reflection on the Art of Living - Ryan Holiday and Stephen Hanselman

The Distracted Mind: Ancient Brains in a High-Tech World - Adam Gazzaley and Larry D. Rosen

The Emotional Life of Your Brain: How Its Unique Patterns Affect the Way You Think, Feel, and Live-And How You Can Change Them – Richard J. Davidson and Sharon Begley

The Magic of Thinking Big – David J. Schwartz

The Power of Now – Eckhart Tolle

The Power of Your Supermind – Vernon Howard

The Talent Code: Greatness isn't born. It's grown – Daniel Coyle

The Undefeated Mind: On the Science of Constructing an Indestructible Self – Alex Lickerman MD

Think and Grow Rich – Napoleon Hill

Unlimited Power – Anthony Robbins

Waking up – Sam Harris

You Are the Placebo: Making Your Mind Matter - Dr. Joe Dispenza

YouTube. (2014). James Eaton. [online] Available at: https://www.youtube.com/user/JamesEatonVideo [Accessed 6 Feb. 2018]

BREATHE

Breathe in Breathe Out: Inhale Energy and Exhale Stress by Guiding and Controlling Your Breathing - James E. Loehr and Jeffrey Migdow

Breathe: The Simple, Revolutionary 14-Day Programme To Improve Your Mental And Physical Health - Belisa Vranich

Change your life in 7 days – Paul McKenna

Head Strong: The Bulletproof Plan to Activate Untapped Brain Energy to Work Smarter and Think Faster - in Just Two Weeks – Dave Asprey

Perfect Breathing: Transform Your Life One Breath at a Time – Al Lee and Don Campbell

The As If Principle: The Radically New Approach to Changing Your Life– Richard Wiseman

The Oxygen Advantage: The simple, scientifically proven breathing technique that will revolutionise your health and fitness - Patrick McKeown

MOVE

Born to Run: The Hidden Tribe, the Ultra-Runners, and the Greatest Race the World Has Never Seen – Christopher McDougall

Evolution: The Cutting Edge Guide to Breaking Down Mental Walls and Building the Body You've Always Wanted - Joe Manganiello

Move Your DNA: Restore Your Health Through Natural Movement – Katy Bowman

No Sweat: How the Simple Science of Motivation Can Bring You a Lifetime of Fitness - Michelle Segar PhD.

Spark: The Revolutionary New Science of Exercise and the Brain – John J. Ratey

Strength for Life: The Fitness Plan for the Rest of Your Life – Shawn Phillips

The Story of the Human Body: Evolution, Health, and Disease – Daniel E Lieberman

FUEL

Always Hungry?: Conquer cravings, retrain your fat cells and lose weight permanently – David Ludwig

American Heart Association. (2017). Trans Fat. [online] Available at: https://healthyforgood.heart.org/eat-smart/articles/trans-fat [Accessed 6 Feb. 2018].

Brain Maker: The Power of Gut Microbes to Heal and Protect Your Brain - for Life – David Perlmutter

Fat for Fuel: A Revolutionary Diet to Combat Cancer, Boost Brain Power, and Increase Your Energy – Joseph Marcela

Integrative Nutrition -- A Whole-Life Approach to Health and Happiness: A Whole-Life Approach to Health and Happiness – Joshua Rosenthal

Michael Klaper, M.D., Nutrition-Based Medicine. (2013). Dairy - Michael Klaper, M.D., Nutrition-Based Medicine. [online] Available at: https://doctorklaper.com/answers/answers11/ [Accessed 6 Feb. 2018]

Natural Born Heroes – Christopher McDougall

nhs.uk. (2018). Others. [online] Available at: https://www.nhs.uk/conditions/vitamins-and-minerals/others/ [Accessed 6 Feb. 2018]

Super Immunity: The Essential Nutrition Guide for Boosting Your Body's Defenses to Live Longer, Stronger, and Disease Free – Dr. Joel Fuhrman

The 4-Hour Body: An uncommon guide to rapid fat-loss, incredible sex and becoming superhuman – Timothy Ferriss

The Bulletproof Diet: Lose Up to a Pound a Day, Reclaim Your Energy and Focus, and Upgrade Your Life – Dave Asprey

The Grain Brain Whole Life Plan: Boost Brain Performance, Lose Weight, and Achieve Optimal Health – David Perlmutter

The Paleo Manifesto: Ancient Wisdom for Lifelong Health – John Durant

The Plant Paradox: The Hidden Dangers in "Healthy" Foods That Cause Disease and Weight Gain – Steven R. Gundry

The Primal Blueprint: Reprogram Your Genes for Effortless Weight Loss, Vibrant Health, and Boundless Energy – Mark Sisson

COLD

Becoming the Iceman – Wim Hof

Biohacker Summit. (2018). *Dr. Rhonda Patrick on the Health Benefits of Cold Exposure and Sauna - Biohacker Summit.* [online] Available at: http://biohackersummit.com/2016/10/15/dr-rhonda-patrick-health-benefits-of-sauna/ [Accessed 6 Feb. 2018].

Wimhofmethod.com. (2018). *The science behind the Wim Hof Method.* [online] Available at: https://www.wimhofmethod.com/science [Accessed 6 Feb. 2018]

CONNECT

A Brief History of Everything – Ken Wilbur

Body Mind Mastery: Creating Success in Sport and Life – Dan Millman

Conversations with God, Book 1: An Uncommon Dialogue (Books 1, 2 & 3) - Neale Donald Walsch

Ferriss, T. (2016). Tools of Titans Foreword — Arnold Schwarzenegger!!! "I Am Not A Self-Made Man". [online] The Blog of Author Tim Ferriss. Available at: https://tim.blog/2016/11/07/tools-of-titans-foreword-arnold-schwarzenegger-i-am-not-a-self-made-man/ [Accessed 6 Feb. 2018].

Homo Deus: A Brief History of Tomorrow– Yuval Noah Harari

Sex at Dawn: How We Mate, Why We Stray, and What It Means for Modern Relationships – Christopher Ryan and Cacilda Jetha

The Selfish Gene – Richard Dawkins

Tribe: On Homecoming and Belonging – Sebastian Junker

REST

Eat Move Sleep: How Small Choices Lead to Big Changes – Tom Rath

Go Wild: Free Your Body and Mind from the Afflictions of Civilization – John J. Ratey and Richard Manning

How to lift depression …Fast (The Human Givens Approach) - Joe Griffin and Ivan Tyrrell

Revive: Stop Feeling Spent and Start Living Again - Dr. Frank Lipman and Mollie Doyle

Sleep Smarter: 21 Essential Strategies to Sleep Your Way to a Better Body, Better Health, and Bigger Success – Shawn Stevenson

The Power of Rest: Why Sleep Alone Is Not Enough. A 30-Day Plan to Reset Your Body - Matthew Edlund

BAD SCIENCE

Bad Science – Ben Goldacre

The Science Delusion – Rupert Sheldrake

Congratulations

It is my deepest pleasure to welcome you to The Tribe!

This is just the start of an infinite level of growth, an infinite level of potentialities.

It has been my honour to be your Primal Life coach but I'm sure our journey doesn't end here.

As we continue to move forward in our separate lives, our paths may cross again.

This could be through my online course or perhaps at one of my retreats, seminars and events – it would be great to see you there!

I'd love for you to share with me the incredible journey you've had, as well as the incredible journey you're still on.

By becoming an example, a doer instead of just a talker, maybe you too can become a Primal Life coach and be the inspiration others need to see to start their own journey in living their Primal Life.

For now I wish you health and happiness with the uncompromisable ability to enjoy everything and need nothing.

At your service always,

Les

Social Media Tribe

Facebook Profile: **fb.me/TheLesterSavage**

Facebook Page: **fb.me/PrimalLifeOfficial**

Facebook Group: **facebook.com/groups/PrimalLifeMethod**

Twitter: **@TheLesterSavage**

Instagram: **TheLesterSavage**

THE OFFICIAL COURSE

This effective 12 week course will carefully take you through the 7 Step Primal Life Method to dramatically change your biochemistry. With me taking you through this at your own pace, you really can become the person you were born to be.

"Lester has helped me immeasurably. A great coach with a superb process that helps you reframe your life in a positive constructive way. He helps you get back to what truly makes you as an individual happy"
– Beverley M, Plymouth (UK)

You will have LIFETIME access to the online private member area with 60+ video lessons <u>PLUS</u> training in...

* Meditation

* Cold Exposure

* Power Breathwork

* Solution Focused Therapy

* Intro to Neuroscience based Therapy

* Most effective principles of CBT and NLP

FREE JOURNAL & RELAXATION CD

INCLUDES COURSE WORKBOOK & 12 WEEK PLAN

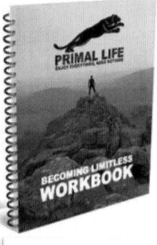

www.LesterSavage.co.uk

www.LesterSavage.com

Made in the USA
Lexington, KY
23 April 2018